The Textile Mil...

Parts 1 & 2

George Watkins MSc

The Watkins' Collection in the National Monuments Record

This comprises the photographs and notes George Watkins made during a lifetime of study of the stationary steam engine.

The Steam Engine Record is an annotated set of around 1500 mounted prints of steam engines which Watkins examined in the field between 1930 and 1980. His notebooks contain a record of additional sites for which no photographs were taken, or which comprise written historical notes.
In all almost 2000 entries were made in his notebooks.
There are also albums of prints arranged by engine type. A catalogue is available.

In addition there are files of notes and other records on all aspects of historical steam technology, the cataloguing of which is in progress.

The main areas of this part of the collection are:

Records of steam engine makers.
Collection of bound trade literature.
Classified collection of data files dealing with,
for example, textile mill engines, marine engines.

The collection can be inspected by appointment.
Copies of photographs and other documents are readily available.

Please contact:
NMR Public Services
National Monuments Record Centre
Kemble Drive
Swindon
Wilts
SN2 2GZ

Moss Mill, Rochdale, Lancs. *see page 4*

Published By
Landmark Publishing Ltd,
Waterloo House, 12 Compton, Ashbourne,
Derbyshire DE6 1DA England
Tel: 01335 347349 e-mail: landmark@clara.net
2nd Edition
ISBN 901 522 43 1

Printed by: MPG Ltd, Bodmin, Cornwall

Designed by: James Allsopp

Pictures

Front Cover: Top;   See Part 1, Plate 76 *Bottom;*   See Part 1, Plate 75

Back Cover : See Part 2. Plate 49

Page 1: The author

Page3:   Petrie's twin tandem compound engine of 1890 built for Moss Mill, Rochdale,
Lancs. The cylinders were 24-in and 45-in by 6 feet stroke. The 200 hp flywheel was
30feet in diameter, working 44 ropes. It was scrapped in 1958.

Page 7:   A horizontal single tandem condensing engine, built 1897 by Musgrave & Son
for William Evans & Co, Darley Abbey, Derbyshire.

Page 123:   The 1903 Hick Hargreaves engine driving No.2 Mill, Beehive Mill Co,
Bolton. This horizontal twin tandem triple expansion engine had cylinders 25in, 39in
and 42-in by 5 feet stroke, generating 2000 h.p. Photographed in 1957.

Page 124:   The Bliss Tweed Mills, Chipping Norton, Oxfordshire,
of 1872. The prime-mover was a Pollit and Wigzell horizontal cross compound of 1918,
scrapped about 1965. Photographed in 1962.

Publishers Note
In the early 1970's this book was published as two separate volumes. George Watkin's
study was quickly recognised as the leading source material on textile mill engines.
The two former volumes are brought together as Parts 1 & 2. Where the original
photograph was not available, a similar one has been used. It was found that one had
previously been reproduced back to front & this has been corrected.

Steam Engine Makers Record.
Part of the Watkin's Collection at the National Monuments Record Centre consists of
material on Engine manufacturers. Landmark are proposing to publish this in three
volumes. Approximately 1000 manufacturers are included. At the time of publication of
this book a final decision had not been made. If you require further details, please ring
Landmark Publishing on 01335 347349 (Fax 01335 347303);
e-mail landmark@clara.net

Foreword to 1970 Edition

It is a great pleasure to introduce this second selection from Mr George Watkins' magnificent collection of photographs. I have already described, in the Foreword to his first book, *The Stationary Steam Engine,* the remarkable way in which Mr Watkins has assembled his collection, during a lifetime largely devoted to the compilation of a record of British steam power, and the strange turn of events by which he came to this University in order to set down in a permanent form his vast knowledge of steam engines. Since then, the University has recognised the significance of his achievement by conferring on Mr Watkins the degree of MSc, and by enabling him to continue his scholarly work beyond the normal age of retirement. He has thus been able to proceed with the preparation of his material for publication, and the following pages represent the next instalment of this material.

The Stationary Steam Engine was designed as a comprehensive over-view of the whole range of engine types from the earliest Newcomen-style pumping machines to the most sophisticated reciprocating engines. It did in compact form something that had not been done before, by presenting consecutively illustrations of all the main variations of the non-locomotive steam engine. The present work is the first of several which are envisaged to fill out the pattern of this preliminary survey in more detail by selecting examples from the main fields of application of steam power in industry, including textiles, iron and steel, coal mining, and the public services. The use of steam engines in the textile industries, and particularly in cotton mills, was so extensive in the nineteenth century, and the wealth of material from these industries in Mr Watkins' collection was so great, that it seemed worth dividing it into two parts in order to do justice to the subject matter while preserving with only slight modifications the format which had proved so successful for the preliminary survey. The following book should therefore be seen within the context of a series, the cumulative effect of which will be to provide industrial steam power with a monument which will be unique in its breadth, detail, and visual fascination.

George Watkins' work has become one of the major research projects of the Centre for the Study of the History of Technology, fitting in neatly with its other academic commitments in the fields of industrial archaeology and the social impact of technological innovation. It is some indication of the value of Mr Watkins' publications that they have been warmly received both by practical industrial archaeologists, seeking to understand the complexities of the machines which they are investigating, and by the academic historians of technology, thankful to him for putting on record so succinctly the story of the development and application of the stationary steam engine. Both the field worker and the scholar will again be grateful to Mr Watkins for this further selection from his extraordinary fund of knowledge.

R. A. BUCHANAN
Bath University of Technology
September 1969

Foreword to 1999 Edition

George Watkins (1904-1989) was a very remarkable man. Steam engines were the enduring passion of his life, and on stationary steam engines in particular he built up an unparalleled collection of photographs, all taken by himself, frequently in extremely difficult conditions, to record the main features of these machines. Over many years, from the 1930s to the 1970s, he made a series of short but intensive tours of the main industrial areas of Britain, having prepared in advance an elaborate programme of visits to engine houses at moments when he could photograph their contents. He was thus present to perform the last rites for these splendid machines, upon the versatility and reliability of which the industrial supremacy of Britain in the nineteenth century had been largely built. But in his life-time they were steadily being made redundant, to be superseded by other prime-movers, and in him they found a fitting and devoted elegist.

I met George in 1964, when he was already sixty years old, and the following year I managed to take him on as a nominal "Research Assistant" at the Centre for the History of Technology which I had recently established at the new *University of Bath*. We gave him the opportunity to arrange his vast collection of photographs and to annotate them systematically, and a first selection of these was published in 1967 as *The Stationary Steam Engine* (David & Charles, Newton Abbot), setting out the main types in the evolution of the non-locomotive steam engine. The favourable reception of this work, by scholars of industrial history and by field industrial archaeologists, encouraged us to proceed with the plan to cover in greater detail the various applications of stationary steam power in industry and the public services, using the same format of large photographs facing pages of explanatory notes. Four of these volumes were published between 1969 and 1979, and it is the first two of these, devoted to *The Textile Mill Engine*, which have been reproduced in this book. In the last thirty years, since George Watkins undertook the significant task of preparing his work for publication, a new generation has grown up for whom the stationary steam engines, the machines which they drove, and the mills which contained them, have all virtually disappeared. For this generation, therefore, the new edition of these volumes provides an invaluable and fascinating opportunity to acquire a sound visual impression of the stationary steam engine in one of its most important forms, elucidated by notes which draw attention succinctly to the main technical features of each machine.

The original photographs and negatives of the 1500 machines recorded by George Watkins have been deposited with the Royal Commission on the Historical Monuments of England and are now held at the National Monuments Record in Swindon, where they may now be consulted by the public as "The Watkins Collection". Application should be made to the NMR Public Services, NMRC, Kemble Drive, Swindon SN2 2GZ. We are grateful to the RCHME for help in reassembling the photographs for this edition.

R.Angus Buchanan
University of Bath
December 1998

The Textile Mill Engine

Part 1

W. Evan's Mill, Darley Dale, *see page 4*

Contents

Twin Tandem

Introduction

S team engines turned wheels in British industry for nearly two centuries. As developed by Savery and Newcomen at the beginning of the eighteenth century, the early engines were mining pumps, and these were later used to provide rotary motion by employing them to raise water to drive water wheels. The introduction of James Watt's rotative action steam engine in 1782 made available to industry an efficient prime mover which was independent of water power sites, and in the case of the cotton industry, which led the way in the application of steam power, this contributed to the concentration of mills in South Lancashire. Other industries followed this pattern, but none adopted the steam engine as completely, or as quickly as did the cotton trade.

Now that many mills have been destroyed or converted to other uses, it is well to remember that a textile mill was planned as a concerted whole, and was a symbol of the owner's pride. All therefore was in tune, so that the mill, the engine and engine room, and the offices were designed as integral features of a single entity, and in this context the power plant was not a mere adjunct to be stowed away and forgotten. The steam engine and its engineers were thus recognised as having a place of importance in the mill. Many of the old mill managers were autocrats, but even they had to defer to the engineers, who ruling their staff with discipline, exacted equal respect from all, particularly when, on the rare occasion of a breakdown causing loss of production, an imprudent manager might invade the engine room with inquiries of, 'Hasta done yet?' The Yorkshire woollen trade also made intensive use of steam power, but there was a greater proliferation of small establishments here than on the western side of the Pennines, so that although one was rarely out of sight of the mills in the West Riding of Yorkshire, the power employed there was generally in smaller units.

As in *The Stationary Steam Engine*, the examples have been selected by types rather than by makers, since in this way design variations can be more readily shown, and the whole more easily divided into two parts. No attempt has been made to describe the types in detail, since this has been done in *The Stationary Steam Engine*, but a brief note on the engine builders will be included in the following part. Since the Lancashire and Yorkshire engineers made most of the mill engines, my examples are largely confined to these, but the immense importance of manufacturers in other areas is fully recognised, since their engines were used far more widely. Throughout, the object has been to present the textile mill engine as a working machine, and the photographs attempt to capture the atmosphere of the engine room as it was. The details of the engines, such as dates, horsepower, sizes, etc, are given as accurately as possible, but records were often lost with staff and grouping changes, whilst with regard to horsepower it must be remembered that almost all mill engines were grossly overloaded in at least one boom time, and the high power became a legend that was not forgotten.

The early beam engines were planned as an integral part of the structure, and so were termed 'house built' (nos 1-4), but in 1784, James Watt built a winding engine for a Cornish mine, which was largely independent of its house, and, as nos 5-7 indicate, such engines gave very good service. Steam pressures increased slowly, and with improvements in machinery the older mills found themselves at a disadvantage, so that they were ready to welcome McNaught's compounding system of 1845 (nos 8-9), and the advantages of this were such that it soon became customary to build engines in this way (nos 11-13). The largest beam engines were very impressive, as nos 14-16 illustrate. Nos 17-22 show other methods of compounding simple beam engines, and the section is completed by considering the side-lever type (nos 23 and 24). The other archaic mill engine type, the vertical, is dealt with briefly, since it was widely used in its home area (nos 25-27).

When marine, locomotive, and portable engines proved that the fear of excessive wear in horizontal cylinders was unfounded, the advantages of the type soon led to its wide adoption, and from usage for small powers, it was soon adopted for the largest mills (nos 28-30). The design was attractive, since the working parts, and thus the working stresses, could be contained within a single cast-iron bed, whilst the small size of the working parts, and the ease with which they could be constructed with limited facilities, made it very popular from 1860 onwards. No 28 is a typical example of the period of transition from the beam to the modern forms, retaining the massiveness of the early engines, yet indicating the lighter form which developed later. As steam pressures rose, compound and triple-expansion cycles were necessary for economy, but it would be wrong to assume that the day of the simple engine was over, since in 1911 Messrs Hick Hargreaves supplied a single-cylinder Corliss engine to Messrs Corn Products of Manchester, with a cylinder 38in bore by 4ft 6in stroke, which exhausted to the process steam heating sytem, and Messrs Scott & Hodgson later made a similar one with drop-valves. Also no 49 refers to an engine long in use as a single. It would be equally wrong to assume that only singles were in use in the 1860s, since although he was far in advance of his times, Daniel Adamson made a triple-expansion engine in 1863, to follow it with a quadruple-expansion in 1874; Crosland of Manchester also designed a triple-expansion single-crank engine which was built by the Fairbairn Engineering Co in 1869. Simple expansion engines such as no 29 long continued to be built as stock work by the smaller engineering shops. The single-crank tandem (nos 28-57) required little space, and was well suited for smaller powers, and within the basic configuration that the cylinders were in line, this type exhibited more variations in its design than any other engine form. The greatest ingenuity was shown in the arrangement of the cylinders, largely to keep the engine as short as possible, to contain the stresses within a single bedplate, and to maintain the alignment of the parts.

The real development of the horizontal compound engine began in the 1870s when boilers for higher pressures were available. To reduce the length of tandems some designers placed the cylinders close together, fitting a block packing for the piston rod in the cover between them, but at least two designs avoided this by re-arranging the piston-rods. One of these, the Pollitt & Wigzell three rod (see *Stationary Stemn Engine* no 19), which was patented in 1870 to give low height and even turning moment for marine service, soon became popular for mills, and, as it was the shortest tandem that could be made, more engines were built to this than to any other special design. To reduce the stress upon the beds of large tandems from the reaction of the cylinder covers, the front and rear cylinders were frequently coupled together in various ways. Nos 54 and 64 illustrate the use of taper cast-iron distance pieces; no 65 illustrates a distance piece also used as a piston-rod guide, whilst no 49 shows one added when the engine was compounded. Forged steel struts bolted to faces on the cylinders, as shown in nos 39, 42, 51, 66, and 69 were also adopted by various makers. No 73 shows a single strut as used by Petries, who, however, also used twin struts in their larger engines. Sometimes the stress of the rear cylinder was taken directly to the frame as indicated by nos 48 and 50. Many successful tandems, however, were built without such stays, as shown in nos 31, 33, 37, 40, 59, 61, 62, 68, 70, and 76. The conversion of simples to tandem compounds was widely practised, and like McNaughting of beam engines gave more power and economy. The added length of the rear cylinder frequently meant that the engine room had to be extended as in no 36, whilst the conversion of no 49 required a 25 ft extension beyond the mill wall. Frequently, however, the mill grew all around the engine room, when as we shall illustrate later, ingenious designers fitted compounds in single space by placing the cylinders side by side in various ways.

Placing the cylinders side by side in this manner was, however, not always a spacesaving measure, as is illustrated by the Abbey Mill in Oldham. Built in the 1870s, this mill consisted of two blocks each driven by belts from its own engine. Comprising a Woolf compound engine upon either side of the flywheel, it was unusual in that there were four cranks to each engine, since each cylinder had its own crank.

Twin tandem engines, ie, those with a tandem engine coupled to a crank on either side of the flywheel, gave a regular turning moment for the large spinning mills, where the type was used more than anywhere.

The mill architects influenced trends, and it was possibly the preference of Sidney Stott & Sons for the twin tandem which led to its wide use in Oldham when it was the greatest cotton spinning town in the world. Buckley & Taylor made many plain substantial slide-valve engines such as no 76, which with steam at 100 to 110psi if not of the highest economy were of unequalled reliability, and after all, with local coal at 7s 6d per ton, fractional economy was not essential. Almost all of different sizes, since engines were then 'tailored' to the mills, a number of these were fitted with Corliss-valve high-pressure cylinders for 160psi in the early 1900s. The latest twin tandems as at Briar Mill (Buckley & Taylor), Times Avon (Saxon), Irwell Bank (Musgrave), or Mitchell Hey (Petrie) were models of efficiency. The last mill type tandem was probably the single crank made by Newton, Bean & Mitchell in 1936 for Blackburn & Tolson of Heckmondwike.

A few semi-tandems, ie with a single cylinder on one, and a tandem on the other crank, were made, and part 2 will consider these, and then the cross compound. This was probably the most widely used type, and the largest engine fitted in a cotton mill was a cross compound of 4,000hp (Hick Hargreaves, 1884). Such engines were very reliable, but the houses and foundations were very costly, and this led in later years to the adoption of inverted vertical or 'marine' engines, as they were termed, which working at higher speeds, required smaller foundations and houses. We owe the finest examples of this type to the rapid development of mill building after 1900, and with the exception of Goodfellows and Urmson & Thomson, most of the Lancashire and Yorkshire engineers made them. The uniflow, thermally the highest development of the steam engine, was little used in spinning mills, but a number were installed in weaving sheds and woollen mills. With this type, completing the whole power cycle in a single cylinder, the mill engine completed a circle of development inasmuch as early engines also had a single cylinder, although they used at least six times as much fuel per horsepower hour. Beside these standard types, a few other designs were tried, and some of these will also be illustrated. The enclosed quick revolution engine was little used in spinning mill drives, but really did come into its own in bleaching and finishing where, operating non-condensing, power was produced at low cost, since the exhaust steam retained most of the heat required for process work.

Although no consideration can be given to them in this work gas engines too played their part in the search for economy. A Mather & Platt Korting double-acting two-stroke engine was used at the Staley Mill, whilst the Hollins Mill at Marple had a 750hp vertical tandem three-crank Westinghouse engine. Both of these were on rope drive and used producer gas, but the difficulty of efficiently cleaning this gas probably accounted for their replacement in later years. Town gas was too costly to use. The diesel engine figured little in our story, but in 1938 one Yorkshire mill installed an eight-cylinder Allen diesel of 1,000hp with rope drive, which ran with great economy.

The first spinning mill in the UK to be built for electric drive was the Acme at Pendlebury, where the motors using current at 400 volts from the incoming 10,000 volt supply, were directly connected to the room mainshafts. Heasandford at Burnley was an early instance of electric weaving shed drive, starting in 1903 with a Belliss triple-expansion engine and alternator, which was later replaced by a turbo-alternator, while the Bliss Tweed mills in Oxfordshire used individual drives on looms in 1907. One of the earliest Lancashire conversions to electric transmission was Ashworth Hadwens at Droylsden, where, again in 1907, the 1,000hp beam engine with gear drives comprising some 90 pairs of bevel wheels, was replaced by a turbo alternator and numerous motors. In the spinning mill one motor was arranged to drive two floors by ropes driving upward and downward.

The power wheel has now turned a full circle. Starting from the water wheel-driven Arkwright and Strutts' mills of the eighteenth century, water power was largely superseded by steam in the nineteenth, whilst today much of the machinery of the Far Eastern mills is turned by hydroelectric power. A very unusual use of water power was at an Italian mill near Lake Garda, where each of the 68 ring frames had its own water turbine.

Some of the engines illustrated in this collection were retained in service for over 70 years, which may suggest that the mills retained uneconomical plant, but this was not the case. The older plants with low capital charges paid their way, since many buyers required yarn quality to be maintained. The products of modern ring frames do not equal the quality of mule spun yarns, but the high cost of fuel and labour, together with the competition of man-made fibres and imported grey cloth, compelled their adoption. The textile power story was one of energy and enterprise, in which management, the consultant engineer, and the engine builder all played their parts. The engineers staked their reputations by backing developments which they thought would pay their way, and the managements took equal chances of mill stoppages; yet but a short time elapsed before some bold spirit gave every development a chance to prove itself.

So there is a fair record of the engines, but little is known of the engineers and millwrights who kept them running. Faced with the appalling chaos of a wrecked engine, they would, with only snatches of sleep on the engine-room floor, work continuously to restore order, ample food and drink being provided on the job. Now all has changed. The engines have gone, and with them, the tradition of work devoted to their service has disappeared, and has even become difficult to understand. It was a vigorous life, which, while requiring deep devotion, gave men the satisfaction of achievement. Yet although so much has gone, all has not been lost in the world of the mill engine. The Northern Mill Engine Society of Rochdale, a group supported only by membership, has done very well by removing several engines for re-erection later, and will maintain the Dee Engine (no 62). The Birmingham Museum of Science and Industry also has a fine series of exhibits, including steam engines which are run on their 'Steam Days'. The Manchester Museum of Science and Industry has several engines turning most afternoons (☎ 0161 832 2244).

Engineering technology developed rapidly once the steam engine was established, so that within 50 years, even the finest crafts were mechanised, and carried out in small factories. The simplest form of house-built beam engine sufficed for such mills, and these differed little from the classic form of Watt's 1782 patent.

1 Giffard & Fox, Chard, Somerset. Lace Manufacturers

This indicates the form that the industrial engine was to follow for over half a century. Its history was unknown, but it worked for nearly a century unaltered, and was believed to date from before 1840. It could have been of local, Lancashire (Galloways of Manchester supplied one of their first engines to Yeovil in the 1830s), or of Midlands make (Haden, one of Watt's erectors, was established at Trowbridge and early supplied engines in the South West). This was a good example of the neat form which the highly developed foundry techniques of the period permitted, and with steam at 30psi it developed 35-40hp at 35rpm. The cylinder was 24in bore by 4ft 6in stroke. The beam, 13ft 6in between end centres, was neatly moulded and ribbed, with the early type of collar-mounted end gudgeons. The flywheel, 13ft 6in diameter, was made in eight sections each comprising an arm and a rim sector, with an internal joint in the rim between each arm, all fitting into sockets in the solid hub. This construction, together with the rounded rim section, the neat fluted columns and governor stand, were all early features. The connecting rod and governor linkage brackets were in keeping with the slight columns and entablature, and at some time the entablature had shown signs of weakness, since it was held

down by timber struts from the floor above. The drive, taken by mortise tooth bevel wheels, was very compact, with all of the major shafting on one wall.

It was in constant use until electric driving, at first from oil engines and generators, was installed in the 1920s.

la The governor, and the main steam and throttle valves were all original. The drop cut-off or expansion-valve, driven by a cam on the crankshaft, was a type used by Watt for the earliest expansion working. It allowed the main valve to work with constant action, ie with free inlet and exhaust functions, and if several cams were fitted expansion could be varied at will. The parallel motion to guide the piston rod was of the usual rectangular form, almost entirely blacksmith made.

Three examples, each by a celebrated North Country maker, to indicate how little this type did, or indeed could, vary in general form and layout.

2 Hartley & Co, Whitelees Mill, Littleborough, Lancs.

Blanket Mills

Made by Petrie & Co, Rochdale in 1841, this, in itself unaltered, drove the mill until it closed in 1948, although a pusher engine was fitted to the crankshaft at one period, and later removed. The cylinder was 25.5in bore by 5ft stroke, and running at 34rpm it had developed 120hp at times, with steam at 40psi. The use of separate slide-valves for the top and the bottom of the cylinder, in chests connected by fluted side pipes, was an example of the way in which parts needing accurate construction were made of small size, permitting large engines to be made with limited equipment. The drive was by teeth on the flywheel rim to a pinion on the mill shaft, although there were two pinions at one time. The stairways and crankpit railings were neat examples of foundry work, and indeed the whole was a charming industrial scene almost entirely in cast iron.

3 Bowers, Roebuck & Co, Glendale Mill, New Mill, Nr Holmforth.

Woollen Mill

Built in 1861 by Timothy Bates of Sowerby Bridge, this worked unaltered for over seventy-five years, and indicates how little the general design changed in the twenty years from 1841 to 1861. The cylinder 30in bore by 5ft stroke, again was fitted with separate valves for the top and bottom of the cylinder, but in contrast to no 2, the valve chests are a single casting only; also, the steam and exhaust connections are above the floor (those of no 2 were below it). The neat fluted design for the columns and rails too was in contrast. Running at 42rpm, it drove by a ring of teeth on the flywheel arms to a single pinion.

4 J. Foster & Sons, Black Dyke Mills, Queensbury, Bradford.

Woollen Spinning

This, the first engine at Black Dyke Mills, was made by John Sturges, Bowling Ironworks, Bradford in 1835. The cylinder was 27in bore by 5ft stroke, developing 50-60hp with the then customary 10psi steam pressure, and 10-12rpm. The mills grew and several sections with other engines were added, and this one was McNaught compounded at the turn of the century by a slide-valve high-pressure cylinder 24in bore by 2ft 6in stroke. It drove part of the mills for over seventy years by a spur tooth ring on the arms of the 19ft flywheel. It was unaltered except for the high-pressure cylinder, but electric drives were installed in the 1920s.

4

James Watt early developed timber-framed designs which were independent of the building and nos 5, 6, and 7 indicate how this was carried out in the age of cast iron.

5 Ainsworth & Co, Halliwell, Bolton, Lancs.

Textile Finishers

Probably made by Cole of Bolton about 1840, the cylinder was 15in bore by 3ft 6in stroke, developing some 10hp with steam at 10psi. The 12ft diameter flywheel with curved wrought iron arms cast into the hub and rim was a very old feature, and the four inclined columns were a direct descendant of the timber frame. The governor stand, parallel motion, and framing resemble Rothwell's designs of that time. Although very slight, it was a rigid design which required very little attention in its eighty years of work. Little used after 1914 it latterly drove the mechanics' shop from the low-pressure steam mains. The beam was 10ft 6in end centres, the whole being mounted on a single cast-iron bed.

6 Wright, Dobson & Co, Alfred Street North, Nottingham.

Room and Power Supply

Made by Benj. Hick & Son, Bolton in 1853, this ran non-condensing, supplying heat as well as power to the tenants in the building; the cylinder was 24in bore by 3ft 6in stroke slide valve. Four fluted columns beneath the beam centre, together with two behind the cylinder, supported the massive entablature which tied the whole solidly together. This short stiff design was also adopted by Hicks for large engines (see no 14). The vertical shaft which drove the four floors was driven directly from a bevel wheel on the crankshaft, and in 90 years of service little repair was ever needed.

7 John Taylor & Co, Colne Road Mills, Huddersfield.

Woollen Mills

Made by Benj. Goodfellows of Hyde in 1856, this, their works no 284, was built with twin cylinders about 27in bore by 3ft 6in stroke, for steam at 30psi. It was later converted to a compound by fitting it with cylinders of 17 and 29in bore, later bored out to 17.$\frac{1}{4}$ and 29.$\frac{3}{4}$in, always having slide-valves. Running at 48rpm, it developed 200hp in later years, using steam at 110psi. The drive was by a toothed ring on the flywheel arms, to an underground shaft by a single pinion. Replaced by electric motors after 86 years of work, it still did useful service for some years, reducing the peak load in winter.

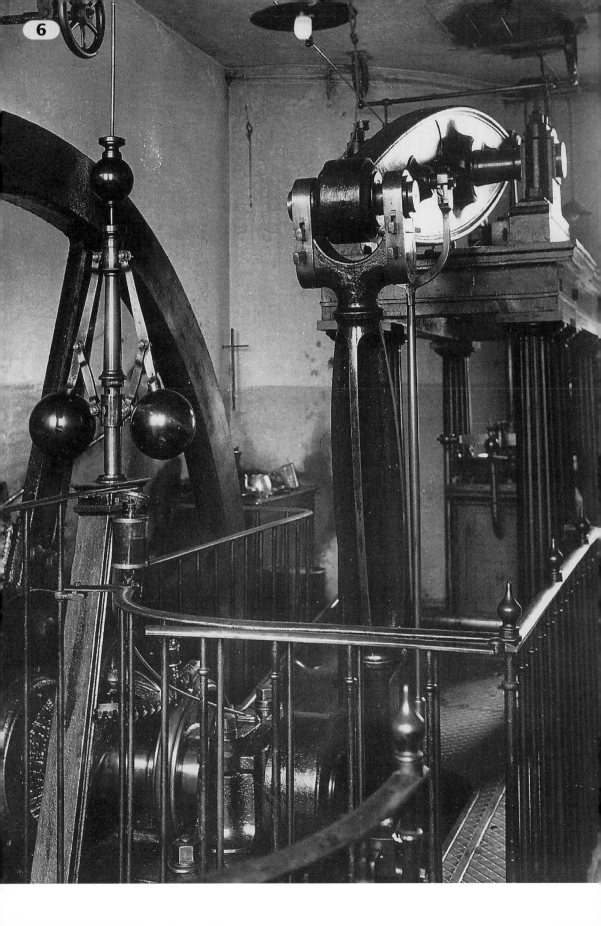

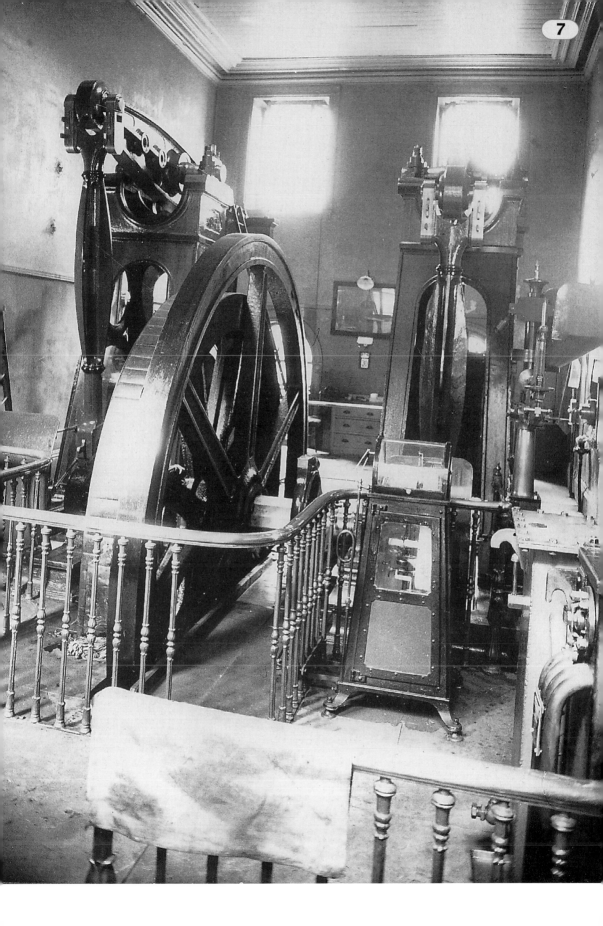

Illustrating medium sized engines of the mid nineteenth century. These worked in Yorkshire, each being built as simple expansion, and later converted to compound working.

8 E. A. Mathews & Co, Eastburn, Nr Keighley.

Woollen Mills

This was built by Wm Bracewell & Co Burnley in 1861, with a single slide-valve cylinder 24in bore by 4ft stroke, which was still in use when the engine was replaced by electric drives some 90 years later. It was McNaught compounded about 1900 by the fitting of a Corliss-valve high-pressure cylinder of 18in bore by 2ft stroke. The beam was 14ft 6in end centres, and the flywheel, 14ft diameter, was originally in a wooden casing, but this was replaced by a neat sheet-metal one after a fire in 1929. Motor drives were installed gradually, and the whole was electrically driven by 1956.

9 S. Bottomley & Co, Buttershaw Mills, Nr Bradford.

Woollen Mills

Built by the Low Moor Ironworks in 1851, this originally had slide-valve cylinders of about 36in bore by 6ft 6in stroke, which, using steam at 20psi gave about 240hp. Some 30 years later it was McNaught compounded by the fitting of slide-valve high-pressure cylinders of 33in bore by 3ft 3in stroke, which with steam at 90psi increased the power to 450hp, and at the same time the drive, originally by gearing and a vertical shaft, was changed to rope drives to the floors. More power was needed in 1926, and it was then extensively rebuilt by Woodhouse and Mitchell, who fitted new Corliss-valve high-pressure cylinders 26in bore by 3ft 3in stroke, together with new beams, which as well as increasing the speed raised the power to 750hp. It continued to give this for some 30 years after which electric drives were installed.

10 Whitworth & Co, Cooperhouse Mills, Luddenden, Nr Halifax.

Woollen Mills

Probably built by Timothy Bates & Co, Sowerby Bridge in 1864, this together with a water wheel drove the spinning mill by a vertical shaft and bevel wheels. Originally a twin-cylinder engine of about 48in bore by 5ft 6in stroke, it was later converted to cross compound by the fitting of slide-valve cylinders of 27 and 56in bore, which with steam at 80psi, developed up to 450hp at 32rpm. Due to the depression in the woollen trade it did little work after 1930, and the mill and engine were scrapped about 1960. In 1850 the concern owned six mills with over 50 men on maintenance alone.

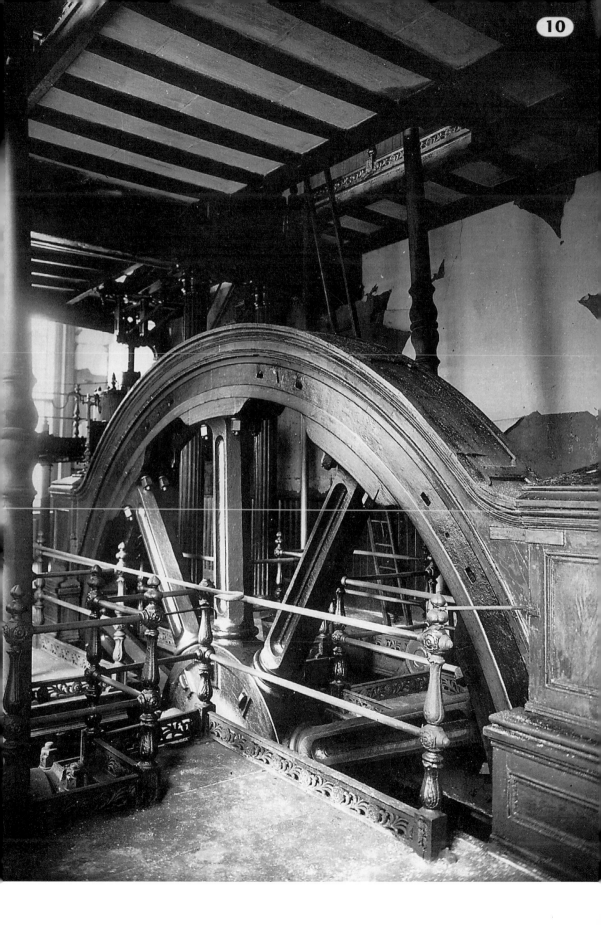

Three examples of the engines later used in the cotton mills where the beam engine reached the peak of its development in later years.

11 The Iris Mill, Hathershaw, Oldham.

Cotton Spinning

Built in the 1860s as the Hathershaw Spinning Co, the mill was fitted with a double McNaught beam engine possibly made by Buckley & Taylor. The mill was destroyed by fire in 1896, but the engine, the vertical shaft, and end wall were saved. An offer was made for the mill whilst it was still on fire, and the new owners rebuilt it for ring spinning. New Corliss-valve high-pressure cylinders of 34.$\frac{1}{2}$in bore by 3ft stroke were fitted, together with boilers for 160psi, the low-pressure cylinders of 50.$\frac{1}{2}$in bore by 6ft stroke remaining. As a ring spinning mill only two floors were needed to use the power, and the mill ran very successfully for over 60 years, but all was scrapped when the mill was closed.

12 W. R. Lees Ltd, Hooley Bridge Mills, Heywood, Lancs.

Towel Weaving

Designed by J. H. Tattersall of Preston, this was probably the last gear drive beam engine to be installed. Made by Buckley & Taylor in 1902, it was a single McNaught compound christened 'Bertha Mary.' The Corliss-valve high-pressure cylinder was 24in bore by 2ft 6in stroke and the slide-valve low-pressure 34in by 5ft stroke, developing 600hp at 41rpm, driving by a gear ring off the flywheel arms. The mill was completed in 1904, and the whole ran with little trouble for 50 years when 12 electric motors were installed, and the engine scrapped. The shed mainshaft was over 400ft long.

13 Lees & Wrigley Ltd, Oldham, no 4 Mill.

Cotton Spinning

This, the last beam engine designed by J. H. Tattersall, was also the last one made for a cotton mill. Again made by Buckley & Taylor, it was a single-beam triple-expansion built in 1904 to develop 1,000hp at 35rpm, using steam at 160psi. The Corliss-valve high-pressure cylinder was 28in bore by 3ft stroke, with slide-valve intermediate and low pressure of 32in by 4ft, and 44in by 6ft stroke. The drive from the 30ft diameter flywheel was by 18 ropes to the several floors. When later more power was needed, a pusher engine with tandem cylinders 16 and 30in bore by 3ft 6in stroke was added to the outer end of the crankshaft. The mills were closed in 1956, when four engines, ten boilers, and all of the plant was scrapped.

The largest beam engines of the textile trade were splendid machines, and the following three examples show the tremendous strides which were made in design in sixty years.

14 Marshalls, Holbeck, Leeds.

Flax Spinning

When Marshalls needed more capacity in 1840, they decided upon a remarkable single floor building designed with an Egyptian motif for the exterior, and this was also carried out in the engine framing and governor. Made by Benj. Hick & Sons, Bolton, it had their characteristic short stroke, six columns supporting a massive entablature, and the very short cruciform centre section for the connecting rod also seen in no 9. The slide-valve cylinders were 54in bore by 5ft stroke, with cranks coupled at right angles, and like the mill there was only a single storey to the engine room. It developed 240hp at 19rpm, when supplied with steam at 15psi, driving by teeth on the 27ft flywheel rim, to the mainshaft beneath the mill floor. All was scrapped when the mills were closed in 1884.

15 I. & I. Craven Ltd, Dalton Mills, Keighley.

Woollen Mills

When the mills were built in the 1860s, it was decided to provide the power from a single unit, and this gave us the largest mill beam engine of which record remains. It was of 500 nominal hp; and designed by Wm Pickup, was built by Wm Bracewell of Burnley, cost £12,000, and took seven years to build. Developing over 2,000hp, it was a slide-valve double McNaught with high-pressure cylinders 45in bore by 4ft 9in stroke, and low pressures of 60in by 9ft, ran at 22.5rpm, and used steam at 60psi. The four cylinders weighed 100 tons, the overhead sway beams, 37ft 6in end centres by 4ft deep, weighed 24 tons each, and the flywheel and gear driving ring weighed over 100 tons. The drive was by two underground shafts, and it was the failure of one of these in 1904 which, by allowing the pinion to roll under the gear ring, completely wrecked the engines, which were replaced by two horizontals with rope drives. The two enginemen miraculously escaped with little hurt.

16 Nile Mill, Hollinwood, Lancs.

Cotton Spinning

When projected in 1898, the Nile with 104,000 spindles was the largest ring spinning mill in the world, and was historically significant since it was the last cotton mill to be built with the traditional beam engine, gear and vertical shaft drive. Designed by J. H. Tattersall, it was a double engine with a complete triple-expansion engine on each beam and cost over £10,000. The Corliss-valve high-pressure cylinders were 32in bore by 4ft 9in stroke, and the slide-valve intermediate and low pressures were 38in by 4ft 9in and 52in by 7ft stroke. Running at 38rpm, it developed 2,400hp using steam at 160psi from four of the five boilers. The pressure was later allowed up to 170psi, and was still so in 1960 when after a very successful life, the mill closed and all was scrapped.

STEAM ENGINE OF 120 HORSES POWER,

CONSTRUCTED BY BENJ.ᴺ HICK & SON, BOLTON.

5 ft. Stroke.

14

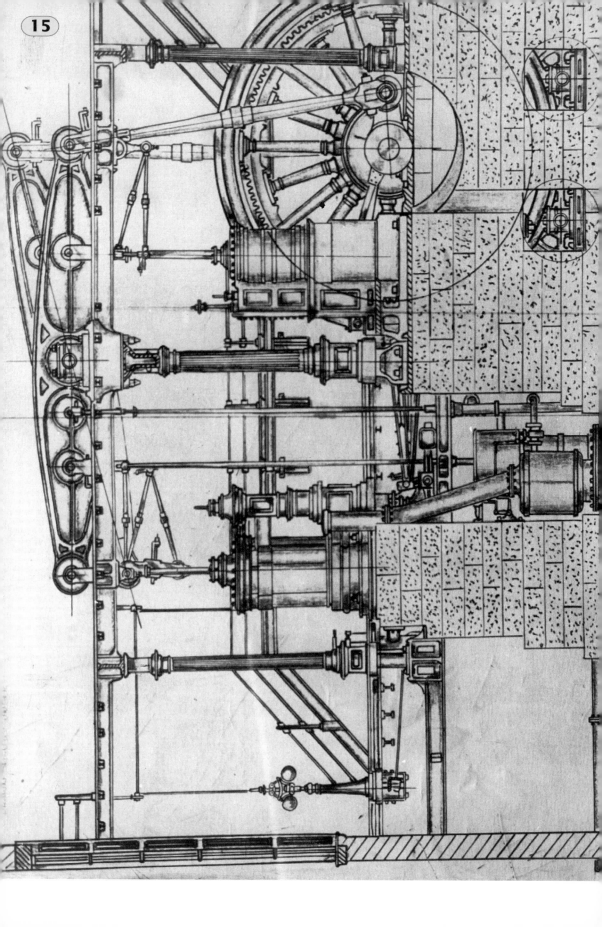

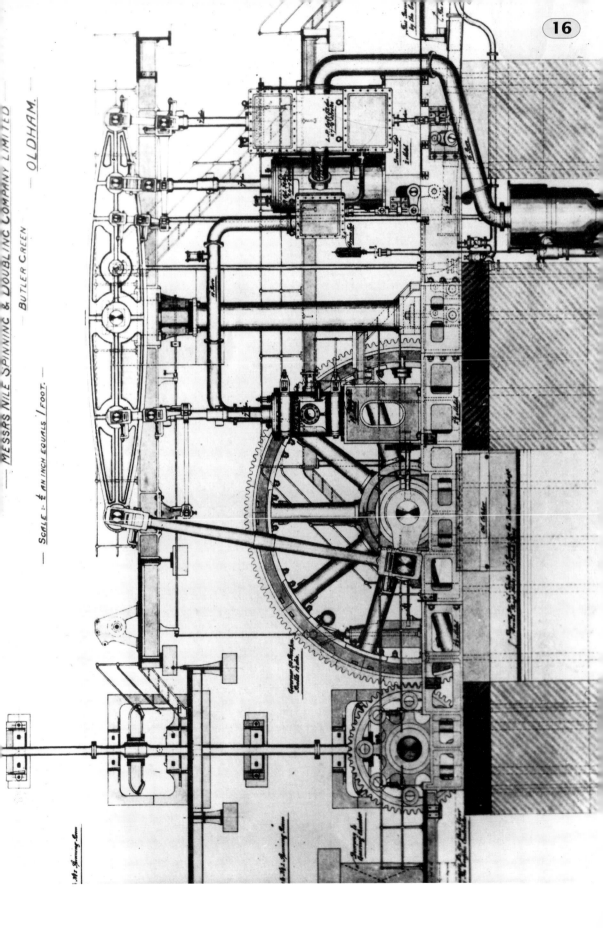

MESSRS NILE SPINNING & DOUBLING COMPANY LIMITED

— BUTLER GREEN — — OLDHAM. —

— SCALE :- ½ AN INCH EQUALS 1 FOOT. —

The pusher was a horizontal high-pressure engine fitted to the crankshaft or crankpin of a beam engine. Less popular than McNaughting, pushers were, however, widely used in weaving sheds. No stress was added to the original engine, whilst since the added impulses came between the original ones, the turning moment was improved. For higher powers the pusher was coupled to the mill shaft rather than the original engine.

17 The Bagslate Mfg Co, Martin Mill, Norden, Nr Rochdale.

Cotton Weaving

The weaving shed was built in 1856, and fitted with a single-cylinder beam engine made by Petrie & Co of Rochdale, which drove by a gear ring 14ft 6in diameter on the flywheel arms, to a pinion on the shed mainshaft. The cylinder was 30in bore by 5ft 6in stroke, with top and bottom slide-valves. The neat cast-iron connecting rod, the attractive fluted columns supporting the entablature, and the open eccentric rod were all Petrie's features, as were the valve chests with the fluted side pipes, the attractive Doric tops to the upper valve chest, and the brass makers' nameplate between them. Rounded off by the pleasingly moulded cast-iron stairs and railings, the engine was unaltered, and was still attractive after twenty years of disuse. It was scrapped in 1964.

18 Martin Mill

As above

When more power was required in 1884, it was decided to pusher-compound the beam engine, and this was done by S. S. Stott & Co., Laneside Foundry, Haslingden, who fitted a horizontal engine and longer crankshaft. The Corliss-valve cylinder was 20in bore by 5ft stroke, and indicates how greatly design had changed in some 30 years; it was interesting to note that, although of shorter stroke, the horizontal was longer than the beam engine. A new boiler for 100psi was supplied, and the added power served until the mill was closed in World War II, although the boiler was replaced in 1930. Re-opened with the return of peace, the mill still functions with automatic looms, but the engines have been removed.

18

17

Nos 19 and 20 indicate methods adopted where space for a separate pusher engine room could not be provided.

19 Thos Mason & Co, Primet Mill, Colne, Lancs.

Cotton Weaving

Very little data survived of the early plant here, but to put the pusher engine upon the wall was surely the most remarkable variant of that scheme. It is possible that Joe Thompson of Colne made both of the engines, but when more power was required, mill changes and lack of space made it difficult to put a horizontal engine bed at the side of the beam engine, so, since the engine-room wall was built of very substantial ashlar stones for much of its height, it made a good bed for the horizontal. This was therefore made to bolt on to the side of the wall, and of large area to spread the loading. The slide-valve cylinder was 21in bore by 4ft 6in stroke, taking steam at 120psi, from the boiler which also steamed the no 2 shed engine. Unorthodox, and possibly unique for a large engine, it gave very little trouble during 70 years of work.

20 Obadiah Ashworth & Co, Middleton, Lancs.

Textile Finishers

Where the factory was on the other side of the engine-room wall, it was not possible to put an engine on the other end of the crankshaft, and a good alternative was to couple the pusher directly to a lengthened crankpin. This relieved the beam of added stresses, but added to the length. The use of an oscillating engine which had no guides, to reduce the extra length, was patented by Crosland in 1859, but it was not widely used. Ashworth's beam engine was of unknown make, probably dating from the 1840s, with a drop-valve cylinder of $42\frac{1}{2}$in bore by 7ft stroke, and developed 120hp at 29rpm, using steam at 10psi. When more power was required in 1901, new boilers for 100psi were installed and the oscillating high-pressure engine was coupled to the crankpin. Made by Scott & Hodgson of Guide Bridge, the slide-valve cylinder was 21in bore, and ran very well for some 40 years until the plant was closed under rationalisation.

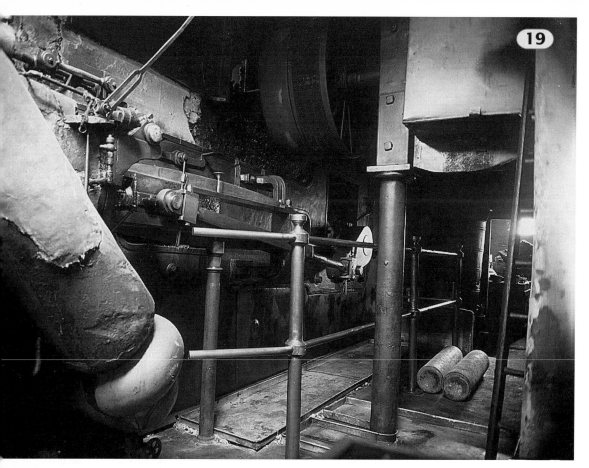

19

20

Compounded Beam—Leigh's & Bagshaw's Methods

Nos 21 and 22 illustrate methods of compounding which were adopted when the engine bed was too weak to take the stresses of a McNaught high-pressure cylinder, and the space did not allow a horizontal engine room to be added.

21

Evan Leigh's patent of 1863 placed the new cylinder beyond the end of the beam and crankshaft, coupling it to the beam by a gudgeon fitted into a pair of side plates which were fastened to the beam as the drawing from the patent specification shows. Although this excellent method did not become popular, at least four sets were made by Musgraves of Bolton, one with a cylinder 15in bore by 11ft stroke, and another 11in bore by 9ft 6in stroke. The method had several advantages. The new cylinder had a very long stroke, which increased its piston speed, and reduced the effect of the clearance, also the thrust was applied directly to the connecting rod, and with the smaller piston, was greatly reduced. It also eliminated the stresses applied to the beam by McNaughting, which as the engines aged, and were overloaded, caused failures at the high-pressure gudgeon pins. It deserved wider use, as beside the mechanical advantages, it was readily fitted since there was usually space at the end of the engine room, where the cross supporting girders could be built into the engine-room walls below the flywheel rim.

22

J. Bagshaw of Victoria Foundry, Batley, Yorks in 1875 used another method. This required a complete new beam to be fitted, with a horn or upswept end which raised the gudgeon pin well above the beam centre line, and so allowed all of the added parts to be above the engine-room floor. The illustration is of an engine which had a very weak bed and short beam. The original cylinder of $23\frac{1}{2}$in bore by 3ft 10in stroke was retained and the added one was 13in bore by 4ft 8in stroke. Running at 54rpm it not only gave the necessary added power, but so improved the balance that the engine was run with the top crankshaft bearing caps off.

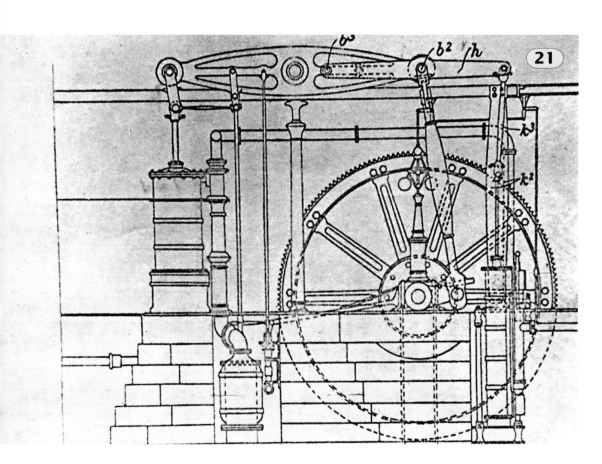

21

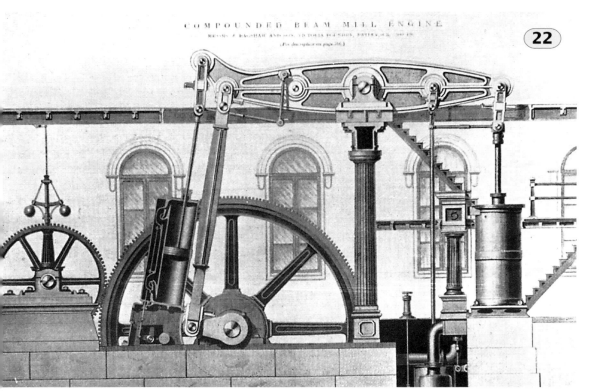

COMPOUNDED BEAM MILL ENGINE

22

This was basically a marine type of which a small number were used in mills. It was very compact, and completely independent of the mill buildings, since, as a marine engine fitted into a flexible wooden hull required, the working stresses were contained within, and resisted by, the metal framing. The foundation was a simple cubic mass which needed little coring except for the foundation bolts and so was inexpensive. The short stroke, slide-valves, and parallel motion of the marine form were retained, but the need for a central drive, ie between the engines, allowed the use of a very simple crankshaft. To keep the engine centre lines close together, the valves and the governor were sometimes driven from the outer end of the crankpins so eliminating the eccentrics usually fitted close to the engine bearings. I have chosen these two examples to indicate design variations even within a restricted framework. Thus Fairbairn's side levers were rigidly connected to a cross shaft which worked in adjustable bearings on the bed, whilst McNaught fitted his bearings in the side levers themselves. Fairbairn's plain cast-iron framing again contrasted greatly with McNaught's forged design which, although light and attractive, was costly, and demanded accurate fitting.

23 Baileys Mills, Staleybridge, Cheshire.

Cotton Spinning

This illustrates Fairbairn's practice and was probably built in the 1840s. The four stiff circular columns used to support the crankshaft vary from the Gothic and other ornate frames of marine practice, but the massive framing tying these to the cylinder tops was characteristic. The cylinders were about 50in bore by 5ft stoke, which with the then customary 5-10psi and 18-20rpm would develop some 500hp. The Fairbairn rim drive flywheel was about 20ft in diameter, driving shafts in either direction by pinions some 7ft in diameter, whose silent mortise teeth added much to an already attractive engine room, but no positive details remain, and all has long gone.

24 J. Fergus, Prinlaw Mills, Nr Leslie, Fifeshire.

Flax Mills

Influenced no doubt by the nearby marine engineering centre of the Clyde, a small number were also installed in Scottish textile mills. Made by J. & G. Thomson, Clyde Bank Foundry, this was a single-crank engine working with a 50hp water wheel, and, designed by McNaught, was the first compound of the type to be built. The design is so compact that it seems impossible to McNaught it, but was done by placing the high-pressure cylinder 'A' beneath the crank and using a side rod motion, which by driving down from the crosshead beams, allowed the whole to sit beneath the usual side lever connecting rod cross tail. Nominally 60hp the cylinders were 22in and 33in bore by 4ft stroke, with steam up to 35psi.

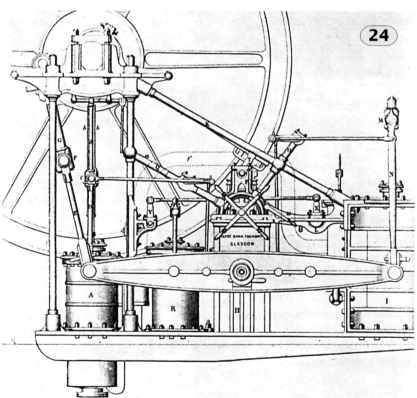

Simpler and cheaper than the beam engine, this type was widely used in the Yorkshire woollen mills. Many were made by Mark Shaw, and almost all of the Yorkshire examples had parallel motion to guide the crosshead.

25 Pendlestone Mill, Bridgnorth, Shropshire.

Worsted Spinning

Leased to McMichael & Grierson in 1838, the plant was water driven until 1863, when owing to the Public Health Act, Wolverhampton acquired the water rights of the River Wharf for town supply. To compensate the mill owners for the loss of the water power, the Corporation supplied the steam plant, the engine being supplied by John Wood & Co, Lock Hill Foundry, Sowerby Bridge in 1866. The chimney, and engine and boiler houses were matched in the local red stone. The condensing slide-valve cylinder was 27in bore by 3ft 6in stroke, the original one being replaced by the makers after it cracked in 1903. The mill continued working on carpet yarn, until about 1932, under various owners, but latterly the premises were a milk depot. The drive was by gears to the upper floor mainshaft, which went the full length of the mill to a water turbine, and drove the lower floor by a belt.

26 Kenyon & Co, Woollen Mills, Denby Dale, Yorks.

Woollen Mills

The history of this engine was unknown, but it was bought secondhand in 1900, and when erected at Kenyon's the original cast-iron framing was replaced by a steel structure. It was compound with slide-valve cylinders 14in and 26in bore by 3ft stroke, and the cranks were set at 180 degrees apart. The two weaving sheds were driven by 12in belts from the 14ft flywheel, and using steam at 60psi, it developed 150hp at 60rpm. The early Watt type parallel motion was unusual in a Yorkshire engine, most of which had the type seen in No 25.

27 Edwin Shaw & Co, Clough House Mill, Slathwaite, Yorks.

Woollen Mill

'Elizabeth' made in 1887, was the first engine made by Schofield & Taylor of Turnbridge, Huddersfield, and probably the last large example of the type to be made. Most of the Yorkshire ones were single cylinder but this was designed as a compound with a low-pressure cylinder, 30in by 3ft, and the high-pressure 14in bore by 3ft 6in stroke. Steam was still supplied at 130psi by the original Hewitt & Kellett boiler when it was over 70 years old. The cast-iron columns, 8in diameter were spaced at 3ft 9in centres, and the drive was by gear and shaft to a four-floor mill, and by ropes to another section. Electric driving was installed in 1963.

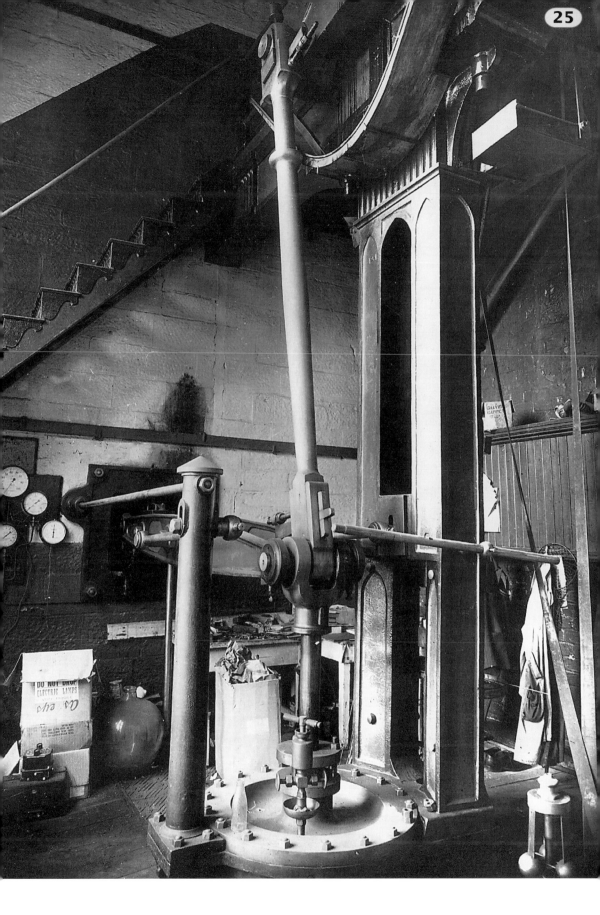

The advantages of this type can best be judged by comparing no 28 with the Martin Mill beam engine (no 17) of some ten years earlier. The reduced size of the horizontal and its house could not fail to attract the mill owner, and my examples give a fair cross section of the range.

28 A. & J. Law & Co, Durn Mill, Littleborough.

Dress & Costume Cloth Mfrs.

Made by Earnshaw & Holt, engineers and boilermakers, Rochdale, in 1864, this drove the mill through spur and bevel gearing. It was condensing, with a slide-valve cylinder 28in bore by 4ft stroke, and designed for 60psi, it used steam at 90psi in later years when, running at 63rpm, it developed 250hp. It was replaced in 1946 when the load had grown to 400hp; it had, for the last seven years of its 80 years life, run 13 hours per day. Its only failure was a split cylinder cover in 1881 due to water, and other than the fitting of metallic packings, and in 1921, a new Lumbs governor (cost £300) its life was uneventful.

29 The Laundry, Nelson, Lancs.

Plant Drive

T. & R. Lees & Co of Hollinwood, Lancs produced small steam engines as a stock line for over fifty years. The designs were plain but in later years were changed to allow the maximum of machining in their construction. My example of this was made in 1908, so has bored guides, in contrast to the earlier design which was similar to no 28. They rarely exceeded 120hp, though at least one tandem compound of 300hp went abroad. My example had a slide-valve cylinder 15in bore by 2ft stroke, and worked non-condensing, since the exhaust was used for water heating. It ran at 100rpm, developing 50hp, with steam at 100psi, driving by four cotton ropes, from the 5ft 6in pulley. The flywheel diameter was 9ft. The plant was closed in 1964 when all was scrapped.

30 W. Rylands & Co, Gidlow Mill, Wigan, Lancs.

Cotton Spinning

Made by J. Musgrave of Bolton in 1863, the Gidlow engines were undoubtedly the largest simple-expansion horizontal engines in a mill for many years. The mill was very interesting in that within the same building it comprised two identical, yet entirely separate half mill installations so that the failure of one would not interfere with the other, or completely stop production. Each engine had two cylinders of 40in bore by 6ft stroke, and later a similar engine was supplied for the weaving shed. Steam was supplied by eight Lancashire boilers, fired with coal from Ryland's colliery nearby. After 30 years of successful running they were converted to triple-expansion, by removing one of the 40in cylinders of each engine, and replacing it with a tandem pair of 19in and 26in bore, which ran to 1915, when electric drives were installed.

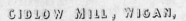

GIDLOW MILL, WIGAN,

FOUR 450 H. HORSE POWER CONDENSING STEAM ENGINES.

J. GOODFELLOW & SONS

Scale of feet

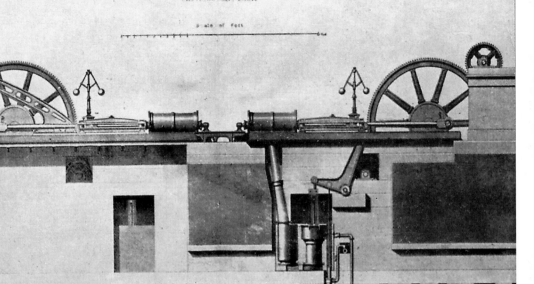

GIDLOW MILL, WIGAN,

FOUR 450 HORSE POWER CONDENSING STEAM ENGINES

PLAN OF ENGINE ROOM.

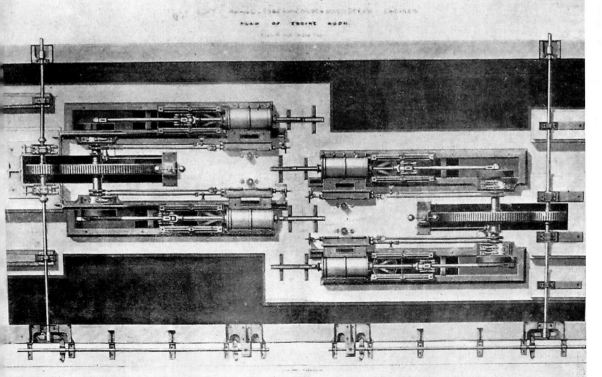

S lide valves, although less economical than other types, were simple and reliable, and so suitable for the lower powers, as my three Yorkshire-made examples indicate.

31 Kaye & Jaggers, Owlet Hall Mill, Elland, Yorks.

Woollen Mill

'Eliza Ann', built by Woods, Baldwin & Co of Brighouse in 1881, was a good example of Yorkshire small engine practice. The cylinders were 12 and 24in bore by 3ft stroke, and she developed 150hp at 80rpm with steam at 120psi. Except for the fitting of metallic piston-and valve-rod packings, and a Lumbs governor she cost little to maintain, and at 81 years old was running perfectly when replaced by electric drives. The flywheel was 12ft in diameter, and she drove by two 18in belts from the 6ft pulley.

32 J. Pickles & Co, Cairo Mill, Cotton St, Burnley, Lancs.

Cotton Weaving

Built by Pollitt & Wigzell in 1886, 'Sarah' drove the Cairo shed for nearly eighty years until automatic looms were installed. The slide-valve cylinders were $17^3/_4$ and $32^1/_4$in bore by 5ft 6in stroke, with a Meyer cut-off valve on the high-pressure cylinder, and she developed 400hp at 62rpm, with steam at 90psi. The drive from the 16ft 6in flywheel was by a 32in belt to the 5ft 6in mainshaft pulley. The belts were of cotton; one of them gave thirty years service, and the other was perfect, after 20 years service, when the engine was finally stopped. The three piston-rod form with the condenser tandem on a single bed were usual Pollitt features, but the open flywheel arms were less so.

33 Jesse Robinson & Co, Royal Mills, Halifax, Yorks.

Woollen Mill

Built by Wood Bros of Sowerby Bridge, Yorks, in 1890, this was fitted with the piston-valves which Woods frequently used at the time. The high-pressure valve was fitted with Woods revolving gear, which rotated the valve several times per hour and so prevented ridges from wearing in the liner. The cylinders were $20^1/_5$ and 33in bore, by 5ft stroke, developing 500hp at 70rpm with steam at 120psi. It was throttle governed, and drove the mill by three belts, 26, 18, and 12in wide, until a fire closed the mills in 1956.

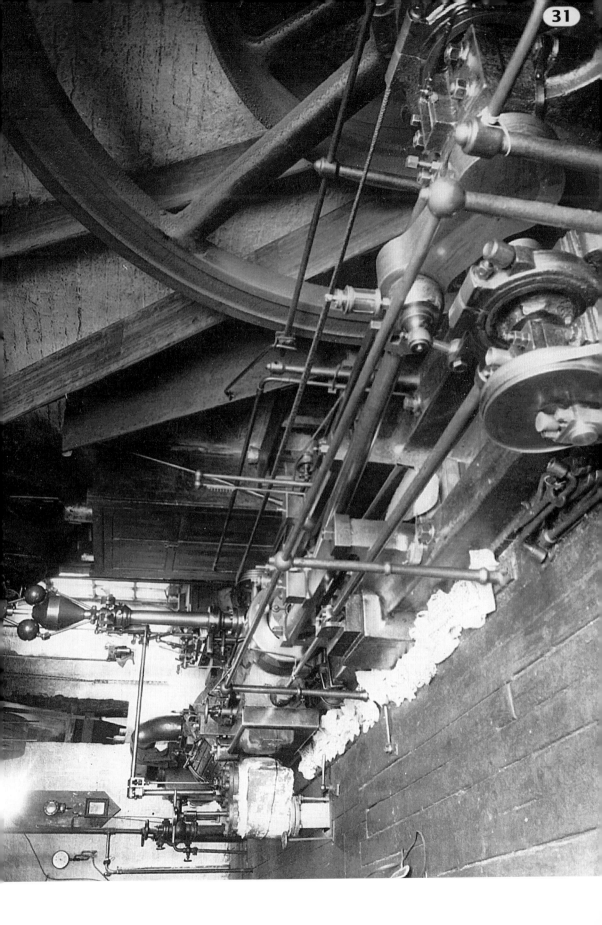

Three examples of small Lancashire slide-valve engines which indicate that practice there differed little from that of Yorkshire.

34 Miles Ashworth & Co, George St Mill, Rochdale.

Woollen Mill

Made by J. & W. McNaught of Rochdale this was their works no 1045, supplied new to the mill in 1905. The cylinders were 11 and 19in bore by 2ft 6in stroke, developing 100hp at 90rpm with steam at 100psi. The Ridcr or semi-rotating cut-off valve on the back of the high-pressure slide-valve was unusual in cotton-mill engines, but it gave a wide range of cut-off control under governor control with little friction. The drive from the 10ft flywheel was originally by nine ropes to the mill shafts, but latterly to two alternators, and the plant gave very good results until the mill was closed in 1961.

35 Robert Hyde & Co, Spring Grove Mill, Staleybridge, Cheshire.

Roller Cloth Mfrs

This mill was originally worked by a water wheel, and then by a beam engine, which were replaced by the tandem in 1897. Made by Benj. Goodfellows of Hyde, it was their works no 964, with cylinders of about 9 and 16in bore by 2ft stroke, with throttle governor only. The drive was directly to the mill mainshaft, from which the drives to the floors were taken by belts and ropes, replacing the original gearing. The bored trunk guides for the crosshead differ from my other examples, but were also used by Goodfellows for large engines. An old boiler on the site dated 1871 suggests that the beam engine was compounded about then. Electric drives were installed later and the engine scrapped.

36 Hindle, Warburton Ltd, Bellevue Shed, Blackburn, Lancs.

Cotton Weaving

This was built by W. & J. Yates, Canal Ironworks, Blackburn in 1869, to develop 200hp from a single cylinder 29in bore by 4ft 6in stroke. It was fitted with a Meyer cut-off valve, used with steam at 80psi and ran at 36rpm. The drive was by teeth on the flywheel rim to the shed mainshaft. When more power was needed in 1890, it was converted to tandem compound by the makers who fitted a high-pressure cylinder of 15in bore, which had cross cut-off valves, controlled by the tall governor beside the cylinder. The engine room had to be extended to install this, and with a new boiler for 120psi it ran well, still at 36rpm, until 1916, when the 15ft 6in flywheel had to be replaced. This again developed faults in 1955, and then the engine was replaced by a 300hp electric motor installed by Whitakers of Oldham, which drove by Vee belts until the mill was closed in 1960.

The increasing steam pressures, together with the economy of Corliss-valves led to their wide adoption, but even so, slide valves continued to be adopted for the low-pressure cylinder in the smaller engines, as indicated in the following three Lancashire examples.

37 Smith Bros, Uncouth Bridge, Milnrow, Lancs.

Blanket Manufacturers

Built in 1903 by the Ebor Engineering Co of nearby Littleborough, this replaced a beam engine. The Corliss high-pressure cylinder was 12in and the low-pressure was 22in bore by 3ft 6in stroke, developing the 200hp needed to drive the two mill blocks. This was delivered by eight ropes off the flywheel, and by a shaft across the open yard to the second block. Steamed by Daniel Adamson boiler no 5799 at 130psi, it gave little trouble until the mill was closed in 1963 when all was scrapped. The use of eye bolts for the valve spindle glands, the insulating casing completely covering the high-pressure cylinder cover, and the Corliss-valve gear on the outer side of the cylinder were unusual features.

38 John Sandiford & Sons, Wasp Mill, Wardle, Nr Rochdale, Lancs.

Wool Dyers and Carbonisers

'Elsie' was built by J. & W. McNaught, and purchased secondhand by Sandifords about 1914. The cylinders had Corliss-valves; the high-pressure was $13^1/_4$ and the low-pressure 24in bore by 3ft stroke. Using steam at 130psi, and running at 73rpm, it was heavily loaded at times. The twin slipper crosshead guides were characteristic of the large mill engines. Two boilers for 160psi supplied the engine and heavy process load, but the drives were gradually changed to electric motors, and, still structurally unaltered, the engine was superseded in 1967.

39 F. 0. Lambert, Lomeshay Bridge Mill, Nelson, Lancs.

Cotton Yarn Sizers

This firm took over the building from Ackroyds, an old established weaving shed, which closed in 1900. The new tenants, who coated the yarn with size for the small weavers, then replaced the beam engine by the Scott & Hodgson tandem, built in 1901, with cylinders 14in and 27in bore by 2ft 6in stroke, running at 85rpm, condensing. The main drive was notable, since the original ten-rope drive was replaced about 1914 by a flat steel belt 10in wide by 0.08 in thick, the join of which can be seen at the top. It ran upon a cork-faced track, which, regularly redressed, gave every satisfaction until electric motors were installed in 1963, although many of the steel belts installed around 1912-14 were later discarded and rope drive restored.

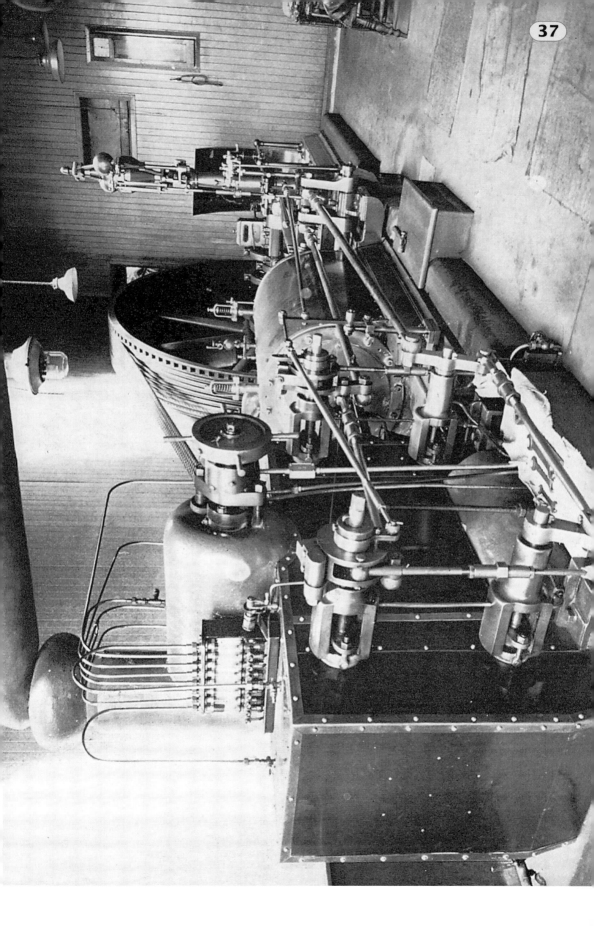

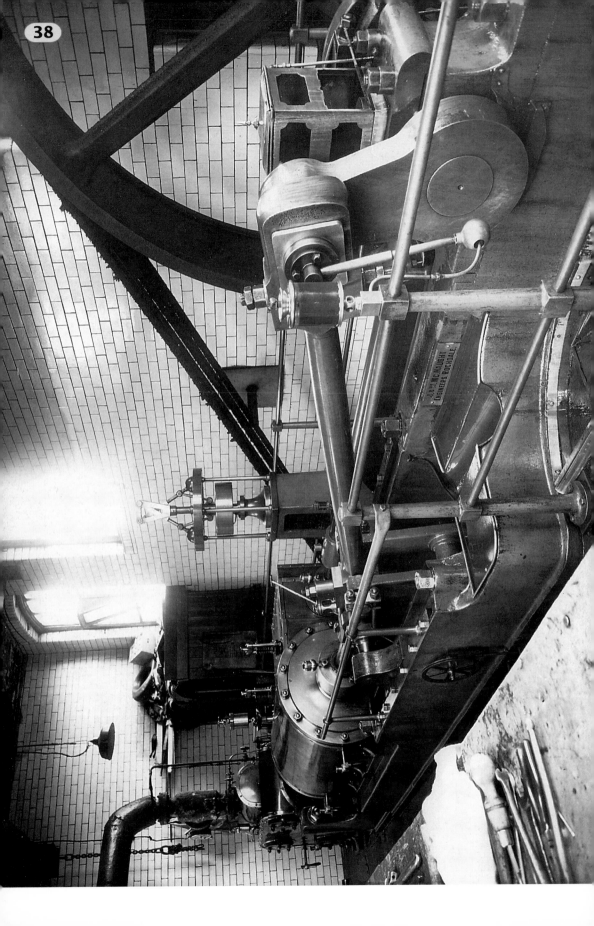

The smaller power required by the weaving side of the cotton trade was equally well met by the single tandem as the following indicate.

40 Thos Hyde & Co, Derby St Shed, Colne, Lancs.

Cotton Weaving

Made by Ashton, Frost & Co of Blackburn in 1892, this was representative of the many shed engines they made over some thirty years. Developing 250hp at 74rpm, with steam at 120psi, the high-pressure cylinder was 15in bore, but the placing of all the Corliss-valves below was not a usual Ashton Frost feature. The slide-valve low-pressure cylinder was mounted on the same bed, which, with the condenser behind, gave a simple foundation. Steam was supplied by a boiler made by Anderton of Accrington in 1891, and the whole plant worked with no alteration until the shed closed in 1960, when only the boiler was retained by the new tenants. An interesting feature was that the shed mainshaft was driven directly from the end of the crankshaft, ie there was no second motion gearing.

41 J. E. Elliott Ltd, Holme Shed, Blacko, Nr Nelson, Lancs.

Cotton Weaving

I have no positive details of this, which is included as an example of an engine made by a concern which later made brickmaking plant. Built in 1900 by Chas Whittaker of Accrington, the Corliss high-pressure cylinder was 14in bore with the slide-valve low-pressure about 27in by 2ft 6in stroke. The parallel swell or centre boss in the centre of the connecting rod was a design feature of Buckley & Taylor, also of Wm Roberts of Nelson, but neither of these provided the boss on the eccentric rods and air pump links as Whittakers did. Steam was supplied by an Anderton boiler which, unusually for a small Corliss engine, was fitted with a superheater. The plant was scrapped when the mill closed in 1959.

42 Queen Street Manufacturing Co, Briercliffe, Nr Burnley, Lancs.

Cotton Weaving

Included as an example of an engine built with slide valves, and later rebuilt with Corliss valves, 'Peace' was built by Wm Roberts of Nelson in 1895 to drive a small storeyed mill and a weaving shed. The storeyed section was destroyed by fire in 1914, and was not rebuilt, but the Corliss-valve cylinders, of 16 and 32in bore by 4ft stroke were then fitted. As in no 42 the crankshaft was coupled directly to the shed mainshaft, the massive flywheel being 14ft diameter. Two boilers, made by Tinker, Shenton & Co, Hyde in 1895 and 1901 still provided steam at 130psi in 1966.

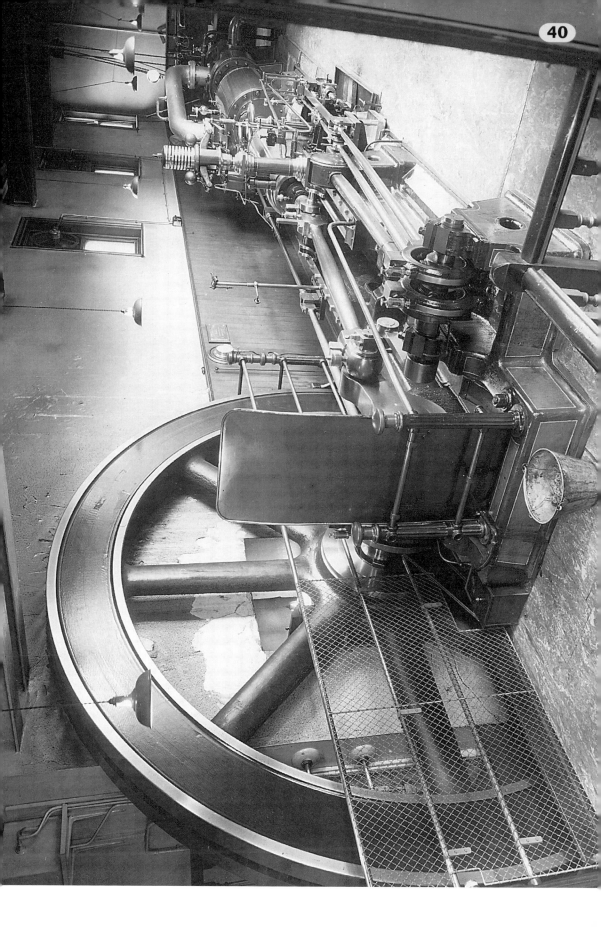

Tandems used in widely differing trades and areas, illustrate a few design variations.

43 J. Slater & Co, Syke Shed, Haslingden, Lancs.

Cotton Weaving

Typical of S. Stott & Co's solidly designed engines, this replaced a double beam engine in the early 1900s. The Corliss-valve cylinders were 15 and 32in bore by 3ft 6in stroke which with steam at 160psi developed up to 350hp at 80rpm. The drive was by 12 ropes from the 15ft flywheel, mostly to the 10ft pulley on the shed mainshaft. An interesting feature was the use of Benn's patent combined air pump and condenser, which Stotts made for some years. This, rope driven, was an attractively quiet and effective arrangement. A single boiler supplied the steam, and the plant was fully in use in 1966.

44 Shawclough Mill Co (1920), Shawclough Mill, Rochdale, Lancs.

Silk then Waste Cotton Spinning

The silk mill, which was driven by a double beam engine, was closed after a bad fire in 1899, and this was one of the two engines which provided the greatly increased power for the cotton trade. Made by M. E. Robinson of Openshaw, Manchester in 1912, the cylinders were 15 and 27in bore by 3ft stroke, with Corliss-valves operated by Robinson's patent trip motion. The flywheel was 13ft in diameter, but the drive was taken from a 9ft rope pulley. Two boilers by Oldham Boiler Works supplied steam at 150psi. Robinsons, together with nearby Geo. Saxons, were the last to build mill engines in the Manchester area, Saxon's last being in 1926. Robinsons did not provide struts between the cylinders of their tandems.

45 Hendersons, South Dudhope Mills, Dundee.

Flax Weaving

Made by J. Carmichael & Co, Ward Foundry, Dundee in 1899, this developed 250hp at 84rpm. The cylinders were 15 and 29in bore by 3ft stroke, with Corliss-valves operated by the early type Spencer Inglis trip motion, and it will be noted that the low-pressure valves were placed at the bottom of the cylinder, so simplifying pipework. Two Carmichael's boilers supplied steam at 125psi, and these were interesting as they were built with corrugated furnaces, an early example of this practice in mill boilers, but the main flues were of the Galloway form. Electric drives were installed in 1966, when the engine was scrapped. Water damaged the rear cylinder head, necessitating the repairs seen, but otherwise little was altered.

Three more Yorkshire tandems which, unlike nos 31-33, were fitted with Corliss-valves throughout.

46 Geo Turner & Co, Owler Ings Mill, Brighouse, Yorks.

Woollen Spinning

Built by Woodhouse & Mitchell, Brighouse in 1923, this was named 'Mary', and started by Mrs J. H. Turner. Developing 800hp at 70rpm, the cylinders were $20^1/_5$ and $40^1/_2$ in bore by 4ft 6in stroke, steam at 180psi being supplied by Spurr, Inman boilers. Superheaters were fitted to these in 1948, and the new metallic packings for this were almost the only replacements needed until electric drives were installed in 1962. The engine was then scrapped, but prior to this it had driven a 135kw alternator. The $28^1/_2$ ton flywheel was in two sections, grooved for 28 ropes.

47 Allerton Combing Co, Allerton, Bradford, Yorks.

Wool Combing

Built by Cole, Marchent & Morley in 1897, 'Annie' gave very good service until replaced by electric drives in 1960. The cylinders were $15^1/_2$ and 30in bore by 4ft stroke, which with steam at 140psi, developed 350hp at 71rpm. The single casting bedplate, with raised scats for the cylinders and frame trunk, and the use of a stay from the rear cylinder to the frame were interesting features, whilst the steel cased lagging was particularly fine. It was scrapped in 1961.

48 Smithson & Gledhill, Ravensthorpe, Dewsbury.

Woollen Dyers

The history of this engine was unknown, but it was purchased secondhand, and installed at the mill in 1918. Made by Marsdens of Heckmondwike, it was typical of their small tandem design in which the cylinders were stayed by a sturdy vertical strut cast with the bed. The cylinders were 16 and 28in bore by 3ft stroke, and until 1954 the drives were all by ropes from the 12ft flywheel. An alternator from a mill that closed was then installed to provide current for new motor-driven machines, but later the load was gradually transferred to the Grid, and the engine scrapped. The process load was very heavy, needing three boilers. It was typical of the workmanlike little engines which, in hundreds, made the Yorkshire woollen trade.

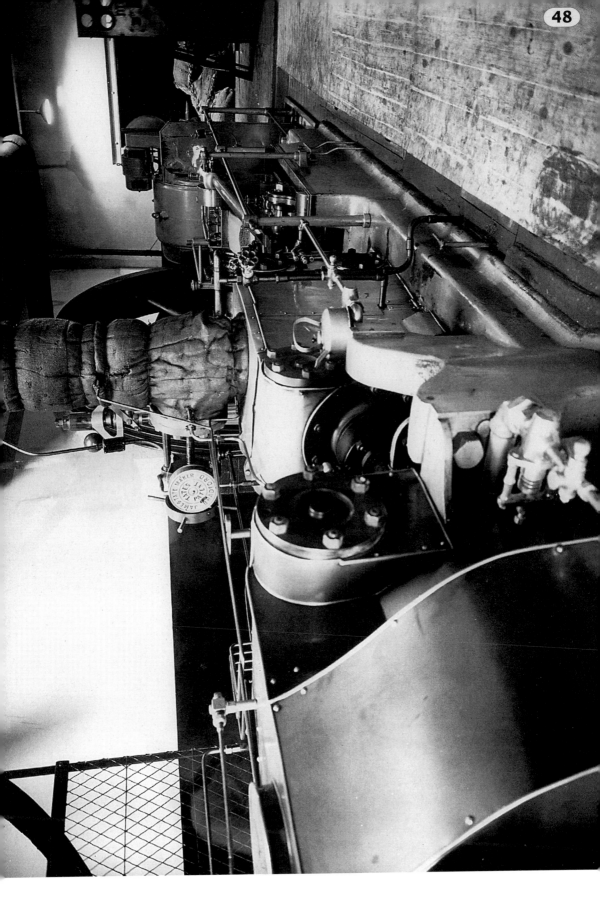

Despite the irregular turning moment of the single-crank engine, its small space requirements made it useful at times even where, as in cotton spinning and large weaving sheds, high powers were required. Three contrasting examples illustrate this.

49 Crosses & Winkworth, Rose Hill, no 3 Mill, Bolton.

Cotton Spinning

Built by Hick Hargreaves & Co, Bolton in 1877, this remarkable engine ran as a single cylinder for 50 years. The cylinder was $39^3/_4$in by 8ft stroke, with Corliss-valves, steam being supplied by four boilers at 90psi. When the boilers were worn out in 1925 it was decided to convert it to a tandem compound, and this was done by Yates & Thom of Blackburn, who fitted the rear cylinder, of 22in bore, together with three boilers for 160psi. It then developed 1,000hp at 57rpm until the mill was closed, all being scrapped in 1960. The single cylinder and massive belt drives were examples of the American influence sometimes met in the 1870s, the main belts being 45in and 38in wide, each driving to a countershaft and by belts to the several floors. The flywheel was 30ft diameter, and as a tandem, the engine was 89ft long.

50 Eckersleys Ltd, Large Mill, Wigan.

Cotton Spinning

In contrast to the last, this was built as a tandem by J. Musgrave, Bolton in 1884, and ran for over 75 years. Replacing a beam engine in the same engine room, the Corliss-valve cylinders were $22^1/_2$ and 49in bore by 6ft stroke which with steam at 120psi, developed 1,000hp at 47rpm. The drive from the 26ft flywheel was taken by twenty-six cotton ropes. Little repair was ever needed; the original valve gear was retained to the end, and on the low-pressure cylinder the charming mahogany lagging also remained. All was scrapped with the closing of the mill, about 1963.

51 J. & J. Ashton Ltd, Newton Moor Mills, Hyde, Cheshire.

Cotton Weaving

The concern grew over the years, adding weaving sheds each with its own engine, and the decision to concentrate all of the power in a single unit gave us this fine engine, driving by ropes and shafts to the several sheds. Made by John & Edward Wood of Bolton in 1912 it was one of the last engines they built. Characteristic of Woods' design, all of the Corliss-valves were below the cylinders which, triple-expansion, were of 14.5, 23, and 36.5in bore by 4ft stroke. Developing 750hp at 77rpm, steam at 160psi was supplied by two Tinker Shenton boilers, which were probably the only 9ft ones they built. Electric drives were installed in the 1960s. The steel struts for the cylinders, and fine cast-iron outer covers on the cylinder ends were Wood's at their best.

Used for many years on beam engines, and then superseded by other types, the drop valve re-asserted itself when the Sulzer and other Continental designs showed high economies in the 1890s. This led to their use in cotton mills as these examples, including one of Continental origin, illustrate.

52 Robt. Marsland & Son, Bamford, Derbyshire.

Cotton Doubling

Originally a corn mill this was one of the last of the scattered early water power sites to remain in use in the cotton trade. The water wheel, 18ft in diameter, was later assisted by a beam engine, and then replaced by water turbines moved from Bollington in Cheshire. With mill additions more power was needed in 1907, and the re-organisation gave us this fine engine. Made by J. Musgrave & Son, Bolton, the cylinders were 16 and 30in bore by 2ft 6in stroke, fitted with the Stegen drop valves which Musgraves used with much success for superheated steam. Two boilers by Galloway for 160psi were installed in 1929, superheating to 550°F. Cotton doubling ceased in 1963, and the mill then passed into other hands.

53 The Charlestown Combing Co, Charlestown, Nr Bradford, Yorks.

Wool Combing

'Dulcie' was installed new when the mill was built in 1912, to develop 600hp at 80rpm The cylinders were 19 and 37in bore by 4ft stroke, and the engine and the two boilers for 160psi were built by Yates and Thom, Blackburn. The condenser was tandem to the low-pressure cylinder, all thus being above the foundation. The rope drive from the 18ft flywheel to a single mill mainshaft was characteristic of the wool-combing plants. The mill was closed in 1958, the work going to other mills of the group.

54 Moston Mill, Moston, Nr Manchester.

Cotton Spinning

Intended to be a double mill eventually, Moston was built with the crankshaft and flywheel for the full power, and provided with the bed for the other half of the engine upon which the outer end of the crankshaft ran. Built by Carels Bros, Ghent, Belgium in 1909, it was their works no 875, with cylinders 30 and 53in bore by 3ft $11^{1}/_{4}$in stroke. Developing 1,200hp at 90rpm, superheated steam at 200psi was supplied by Tetlow boilers. The flywheel, 19ft in diameter, was provided with the sixty rope grooves that the full power would have required. The second half of the mill, however, was never completed, and in 1958 electric drives were installed, and the engine was scrapped. Typical of Continental design, six or more of Carels' engines were installed in Lancashire mills in the early 1900s.

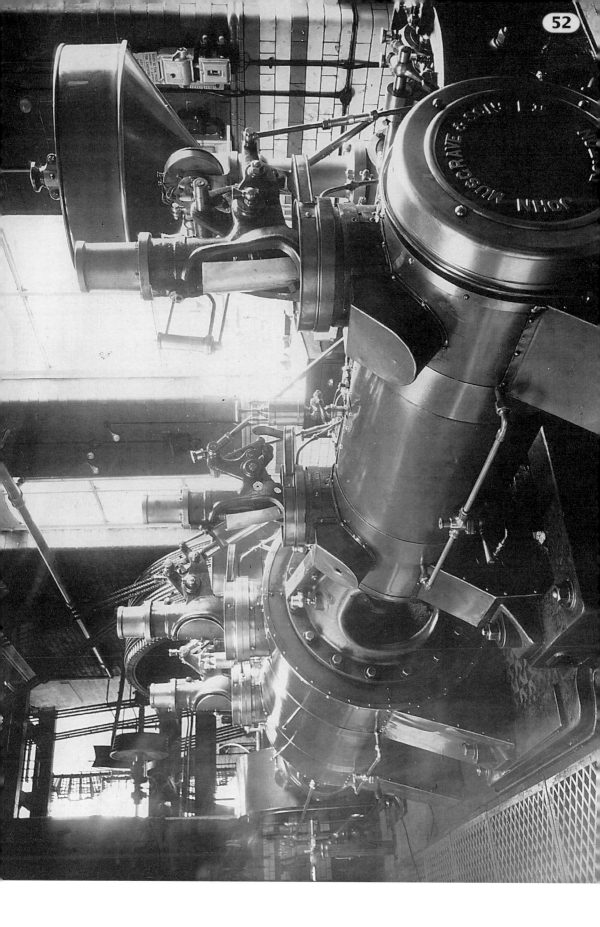

Yorkshire and Scottish examples of the later drop-valve trend. No 55 illustrates that not all were simply copies of Continental designs since it retains the characteristic Pollitt frame.

55 Thos Henry Shaw & Co, Wapping Mills, Bradford, Yorks.

Woollen Mills

When the mills were built in 1911, they were provided with the best engines that Yorkshire could supply. One half was driven by this Pollitt & Wigzell engine which, although it was provided with drop-inlet valves, was fitted with Corliss type exhausts, so keeping all of the working parts above the floor. Developing 500hp at 82rpm, the cylinders were 18 and 34in bore by 4ft stroke, with steam at 140psi. Contrasting with Pollitt's more usual three piston-rod form (see *Stationary Steam Engine* no 19), the cylinders were separate here, with a single piston-rod only and with a supporting pad between the high-and low-pressure cylinders. The drop-piston valves were very quiet. The usual single-shaft drive of the woolcombing shed was provided, but with a generator drive as well.

56 Thos Henry Shaw

As above

The other engine was in the same room, with a similar drive. Also built in 1911, this too, was of 500hp, but was made by Cole Marchent & Morley, and fitted with their drop-piston valves. These worked in ported liners and were very quiet even at the highest speeds. Working at higher speed, ie 102rpm, the cylinders were smaller, $17^3/_4$ and 30in bore by 3ft stroke, supplied with steam from the same four boilers which not only supplied the two engines noted, but also a 500hp uniflow, and the process load, at 140psi. The drive was from the 13ft flywheel by twelve ropes. Electric drives were installed in the early 1960s and the engines were scrapped.

57 Ogilvie Bros, Kirriemuir, Perthshire.

Flax Mills

Made by Douglas & Grant, Kirkaldy in 1915, this was their works no 700, designed to develop 350hp at 80rpm, with steam at 120psi. The cylinders were 14 and 28in bore by 2ft stroke with drop-valves. The flywheel was 12ft 6in diameter, and drove by eight ropes to the shed mainshaft which was below the shed floor, all of the looms being driven by belts which came up through slots in the floor. This made the shed much lighter than with the usual overhead drive. There were two sheds, each originally with its own engine, and one of these was replaced by motors after a breakdown. Motors were being installed to replace this engine as well in 1965.

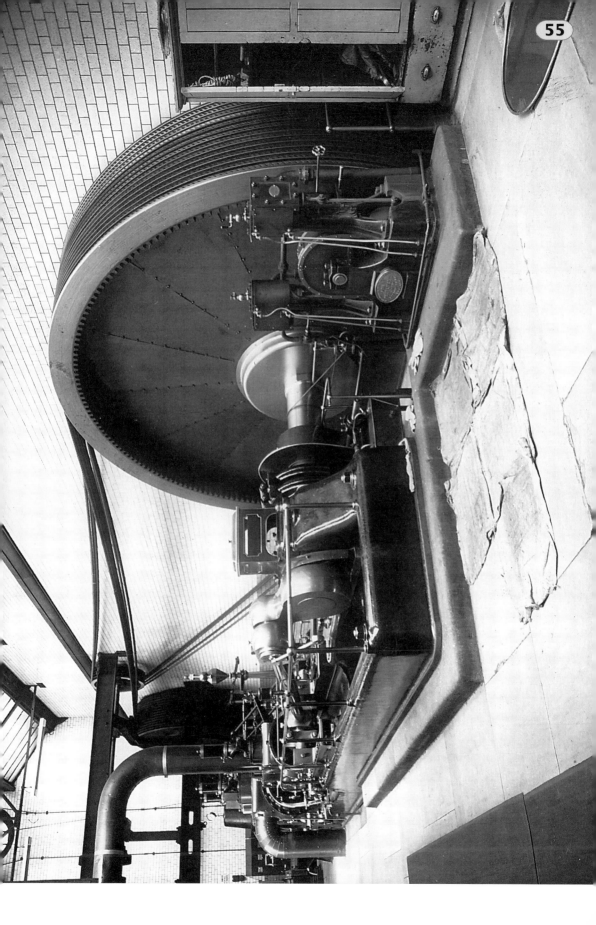

These were high-power units, and so usually found in the large cotton spinning mills, as the following examples of the compound type indicate.

58 Ross Spinning Mill, Bacup, Lancs.

Cotton Spinning

The Ross was planned as a twin mill, and the first half was completed in 1912, one side of the engine being installed to run it. The other side of the engine was put on in 1921 but by then the cost of building had increased so greatly that the other half of the mill was never built. Even so, the intensive machining of the one half mill sometimes loaded the engine to 3,000hp, and at one time when one side of the engine failed, the other side carried 2,000hp until the repairs were completed. The Corlissvalve cylinders were 26in and 54in bore by 5ft stroke, running at 70rpm, using steam at 160psi. The flywheel of 27ft diameter was grooved for 66 cotton ropes, and except for a failure on one side of some ten days duration it gave little trouble until replaced by motors in 1963-4.

59 Hartford Mill, Werneth, Oldham, Lancs.

Cotton Spinning

Hartford was the mill in which Platt Bros of Oldham tried out the various new designs of plant they introduced, and the engine was almost certainly the only twin tandem that Urmson & Thompson constructed. Built in 1907, and named 'Oldham', the Corliss-valve cylinders were 21in and 44in bore by 5ft stroke, and it developed 1,500hp at 65rpm, using steam at 170psi. The drive was by 34 ropes from the 24ft flywheel, but all was scrapped when, in 1957 electric drives were installed. It seems incredible that such an engine was built for £5,400, and its three boilers for £1,900. That, however, was the cost of this very good plant.

60 Lion Mill, Royton, Lancs.

Cotton Spinning

Lion was built in 1890 with 109,000 spindles, then the largest number in a single mill and the engine was sized accordingly. Built by Pollitt & Wigzell, Sowerby Bridge, Yorks, it developed 2,000hp, from piston-valve cylinders of 27 and 46in bore by 5ft 6in stroke on each side, but these proved uneconomical. In 1900, therefore, Pollitts replaced them by Corliss-valve cylinders, which were very satisfactory. The replacement was made in 14 days, a record for a job of such magnitude even then. The original six boilers for 100psi were retained, but when these were condemned in 1952, the mill was converted to electric drive by fitting large motors in the rope race, replacing the 40-rope drive from the 22ft 6in flywheel.

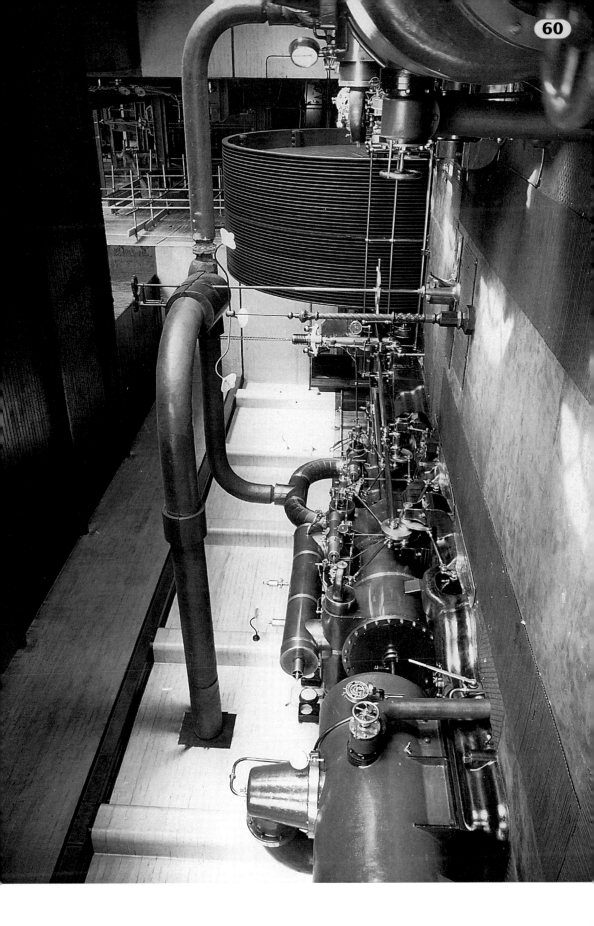

61 State Mill, Woodbine St, Rochdale, Lancs.

Cotton Spinning

When an engine builder received an inquiry for a new engine, it was customary to have a show engine in the district which the potential customer might inspect. State fulfilled this function for J. & W. McNaught of Rochdale, who built it in 1901. Designed to develop 1,600hp, it was a twin tandem with Corliss-valve high-pressure cylinders of 21in and piston-valve low pressures of 44in bore by 5ft stroke, running at 65rpm, on steam at 160psi. The five mill floors were driven by 38 ropes from the 24ft flywheel, but all was scrapped when, acquired by new owners in 1955, the mill was converted to electric drives.

62 Dee Mill, Shaw, Lancs.

Cotton Spinning

One of the few twin tandem mill engines built by Scott & Hodgson, this was made in 1907. The Corliss-valve high-pressure cylinders were 21in bore, and the piston-valve low pressures were 44in bore, all by 5ft stroke. Running at 65rpm, they were designed to develop 1,500hp, steam being supplied by four boilers by Joseph Adamson of Hyde, which, designed for 200psi in 1907, were still insured for that 60 years later. The mill was gradually changed over to electric drive, and when this was completed in 1968, the owners gracefully permitted the engine to remain in position, under the care of The Northern Mill Engines Society of Rochdale, a worthy end for a good servant.

63 The Perseverance Mill Co, Padiham, Lancs.

Cotton Weaving

The smaller powers required by the weaving sheds (usually below 600hp) could be economically supplied by compound engines. When, however, very large sheds employing 2,000 looms, and so needing over 1,000hp were planned, the higher economy of the triple-expansion engine justified its extra cost. The Burnley Ironworks Co made two similar engines for the Peel, and Perseverance sheds, and 'Isabel and Martha' was built for Perseverance shed in 1906, and designed to develop 1,200hp. The high-and intermediate-pressure cylinders were 18 and 28in bore, with Corliss-valves and trip motion, but the two low-pressure cylinders, each 29in bore, and nearest to the crankshaft, were fitted with semi-rotary slide valves. All were of 5ft stroke. Running at 56rpm, it drove the shed mainshaft by twenty-four ropes. Steam was supplied at 180psi by three Yates and Thom boilers, which were converted to oil firing in 1956. The gradual change to electric drive was completed in 1962, when the engine was scrapped.

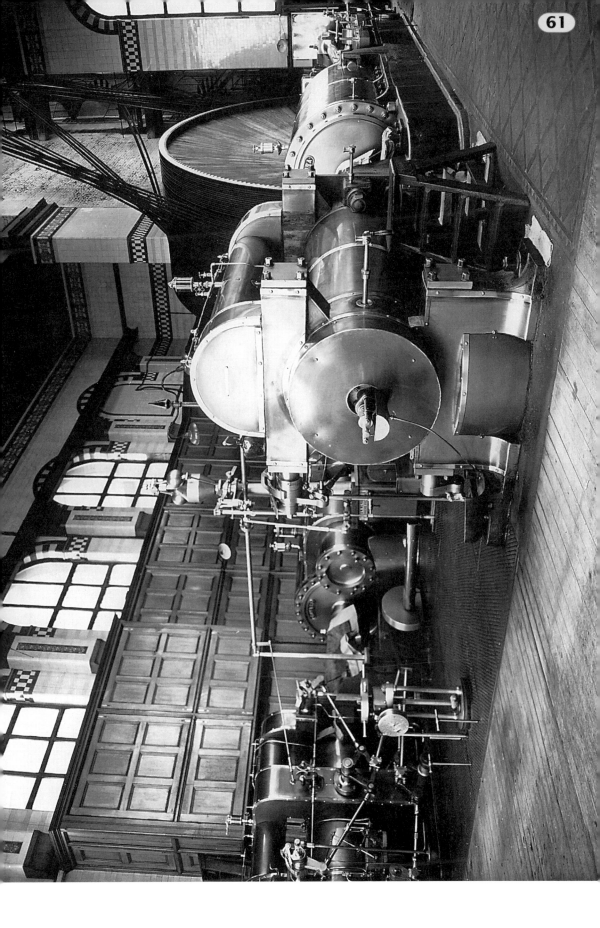

The six examples of this type which follow, indicate the highest development of the English tandem mill engine.

64 The Lancashire Cotton Corporation, Wilton Mill, Radcliffe.

Cotton Spinning

Wilton was powered by one of the few large engines which Galloways supplied to the Lancashire mills. Built in 1907, it was fitted with Corliss-valves to all of the four cylinders, which, designed to develop 1,600hp, had to provide 2,000hp at times. The cylinders were 26, 36, 40, and 40in bore by 5ft stroke, and running at 63rpm, it used steam at 170psi from four boilers. The drive from the 26ft flywheel was by 36 ropes, and the engine was interesting on account of having four-bar crosshead guides. The mill was closed in 1964, when, in other usage, the whole plant was scrapped.

65 Ashton Bros, Throstle Bank Mill, Hyde, Cheshire.

Cotton Spinning

Built by Benjamin Goodfellows in 1895, this was their works no 907. The cylinders were 21, 31.5, 33, and 33in bore by 5ft stroke, all with Corliss valves, and using steam at 160psi, it developed 1,400hp, at 60rpm. Originally fitted with Goodfellows, or Ramsbottom trip gear, this was replaced by Saxons on the intermediate cylinder, and a complete new high-pressure cylinder and valve gear was fitted by Scott & Hodgsons. The drive was by forty-two ropes from the 30ft flywheel, but all was scrapped when the mill was changed to motor drives in 1956-7.

66 The Lancashire Cotton Corporation, Rock Mill, Ashton-Under-Lyne.

Cotton Spinning

Built in 1892, Rock illustrates the compactness of the gear drive, since all of the driving gear for the upper floors was in a shaft tower on the right, outside of the mill. Built by George Saxon, and called 'Egypt' and 'Ashton', the engine was fitted with Corliss-valve cylinders of 22, 36, 40, and 40in bore, all by 6ft stroke. The original gear drive was by a separate wheel on the crankshaft, and when trouble developed with this in the 1950s, it is a high tribute to the engineers of the LCC, and the millwrights, that they replaced it with a set of differing sizes from another mill. The original boilers, for 160psi, were replaced by three Tinker Shenton's for 180psi in 1913 to give more power. Rock mill was sold in 1960, when with the change to other fibres, the existing plant was scrapped.

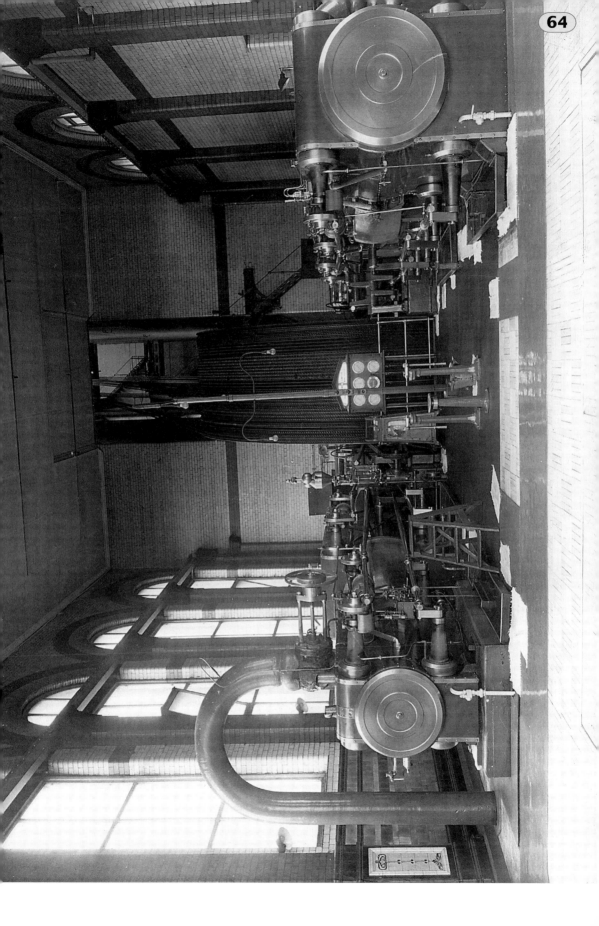

67 The Lancashire Cotton Corporation, Imperial Mill, Blackburn.

Cotton Spinning

Built by Yates & Thom in 1901, and called 'King Edward Vll', and 'Queen Alexandra', this was designed to develop 1,700hp. The cylinders were 25, $38^1/_5$, $42^5/_8$ and $42^5/_8$in bore by 5ft 6in stroke, running at $65^1/_2$rpm, and using steam at 180psi. The drive was by 38 ropes from the 27ft flywheel. The Dobson Corliss trip gear, and the trunk type main frames were features of Yates & Thom's later designs. It was in perfect condition when, with the installation of electric drives, it was scrapped in 1963.

68 The Eclipse Mill, Rochdale, Lancs.

Cotton Spinning

Built in 1900 the Eclipse was a large mill, with 118,000 spindles. Called 'Century', the engine was made by J. & W. McNaught, to develop 1,700hp at 67rpm, using steam at 180psi from four boilers. The Corliss-valve high-pressure cylinder was 24in bore, with a 38in intermediate, and two 42in bore low-pressures with piston valves, all by 5ft stroke. In later years, there was continuous trouble over smoke from poor fuel, which caused a change to electric drives in the 1950s, but the mill was closed a few years later.

69 The Lancashire Cotton Corporation, Trencherfield Mill, Wigan.

Cotton Spinning

Built new with the mill in 1907, this engine christened 'Rina' and 'Helen', was the largest engine built by the makers, John & Edward Wood of Bolton. Designed to develop 2,500hp at $67^3/_4$rpm, it was triple-expansion with Corliss-valve cylinders $25^1/_8$-$40^3/_8$in and two $44^1/_4$in bore low-pressures, all by 5ft stroke, driving by 54 ropes from the 26ft 6in flywheel. Steam at 200psi was provided by six boilers by Tinker, Shenton & Co of Hyde which, built for 200psi in 1907, were still insured for this pressure in 1967. The furnace tubes were $^3/_4$ in thick. Frequently overloaded, it gave little trouble until it was replaced by motor driven machines in 1966-7. The steel struts between the cylinders were a usual feature of Woods' engines while the use of Corliss-valves all placed below the cylinders was their standard design for some 40 years.

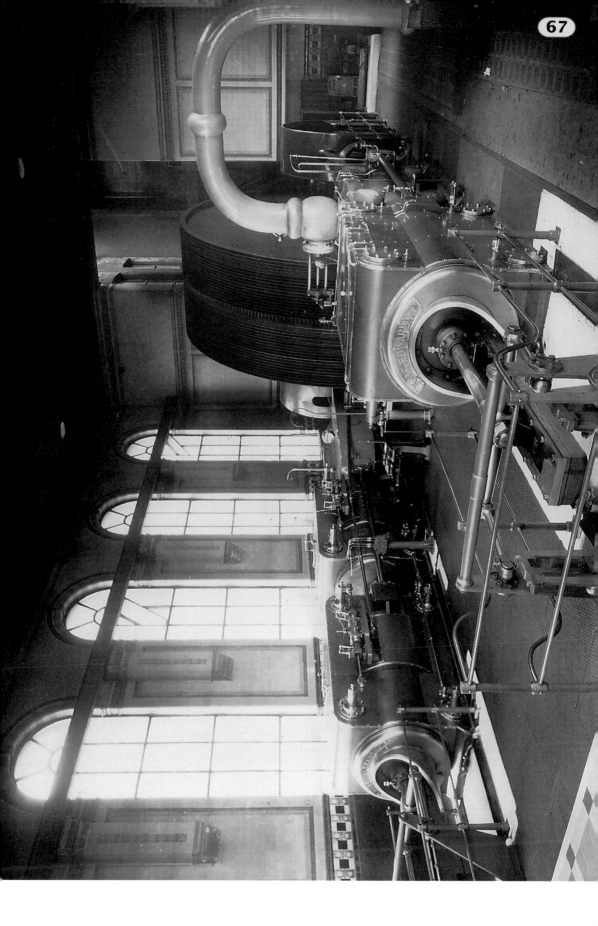

The older heavily made engines were often uneconomic to run long before they were worn out, and reference has been made to methods of remedying this. With the increasing use of electric power in recent years, such schemes were less popular, so this record of the last of them is included to indicate what occurred.

70 Broadbent & Co, Oakfield Mill, Droylsden, Lancs.

Cotton Spinning & Weaving

The spinning mill engine was a twin tandem slide valve. The last of Woolstenhulme & Rye's engines to remain as built, it was their works no 272 of 1878, with cylinders 16 and 30in bore by 5ft stroke, developing 900hp at 65rpm. The speed was controlled by varying the cut-off in the high-pressure cylinders, by means of a 'puff and dart' motion, which worked the cut-off plates on the back of the valves through the steam and air dashpots seen above and between the high-pressure valve chests. In its first 75 years of work little was altered except to fit metallic packings and a high speed governor, and to add piston-rod supports between the cylinders.

71 Broadbents

As above

In 1953, increasing load, and the need in any case to rebore the high-pressure cylinders led to the decision to replace them completely. The work was entrusted to Wainwrights of Staleybridge, and this shows the job proceeding. With the single exception of a projection below one cylinder, which could neither be seen nor measured, every detail was so accurately dealt with that all went according to plan, and the installation was completed in the fortnight wakes holiday, a tribute to all concerned. The fitter working inside the right-hand low-pressure cylinder was scraping down a ridge at the end of the bore.

72 Broadbents

As above

Taken a few weeks after she was re-started with the new cylinders, this shows how Wainwrights maintained the engineer tradition, in not only knowing what to do, but how to do it. The Corliss-valves gave considerable economy of fuel, and this with the saving of cylinder oil would pay for the work in five years.

It will be noted that the rest of the engine was untouched, retaining the four-bar crosshead guides, and the twenty-rope drive from the 24ft flywheel. The two Hewett & Kellett boilers for 120psi were also retained. The estimated economies were realised, paying for the work, when some five years later trade difficulties caused the closure of the mill and all was scrapped.

These were influenced by the constant search for economy, and also when a concern appointed a new designer. Two concerns will serve to illustrate this feature, viz, John Petrie & Co, Rochdale (established 1816), and Buckley & Taylor, Oldham (established 1861).

JOHN PETRIE AND CO, WHITEHALL ST, ROCHDALE

73 Brierfield Mills, Brierfield, Nr Burnley, Lancs.

Cotton Spinning and Weaving

Following the successful use of piston-valves on their beam engines, Petries continued to use them on their horizontal engines, of which Brierfield had three, all triple expansion. The spinning mill engine, probably replacing a beam engine, was built in 1894 to develop 1,500hp at 57rpm. The cylinders were 24, 36, 42, and 42in bore by 5ft stroke, all with twist cut-off piston-valves, and with internal valves for the high-and intermediate-cylinders. The low-pressure cylinders were nearer to the cranks, each with its own condenser, with air pumps driven from the crankpins. The 24ft flywheel drove by 36 ropes. Eight Petrie boilers provided steam at 160psi for the three Petrie, and one Burnley Ironworks engines, all of which were scrapped when another group took the mills in 1959.

74 The Era Mill, Woodbine St, Rochdale, Lancs.

Cotton Spinning

'Victoria', built by Petries in 1898 differed from no 73 in having Corliss-valves for the high-and intermediate-cylinders (although the low-pressures still had piston-valves) and in having the air pumps at the rear of the engine. Designed to develop 1,500hp at 65rpm, the cylinders were 24, 36, 42, and 42in bore by 5ft stroke, with the drive from the 26ft flywheel by 40 ropes. Four Petrie boilers supplied steam at 160psi, and were still doing so when 60 years old. Except for the fitting of a new design of high-pressure cylinder in 1904, little was changed in its 60 years of life, which ended when, in 1958, the mill was converted to electric drive.

75 Roger Shackleton & Co, Mitchell Hey Mill, Rochdale.

Cotton Spinning and Weaving

John Petrie & Co could not be said to stand still, as following on the proved economy of the Continental drop-valve engines, they engaged a Swiss, Mr Nuekomm, to design one for them, and it was very good. This twin tandem compound, built in 1909 with cylinders of 19 and 38in bore by 4ft stroke, developed 1,400hp with little trouble for 50 years, on steam at 180psi. It is notable that after using a trunk frame for many years, Petries with a Continental designer, reverted to an old flat form bed, driving the air pumps from below the crosshead by a beam. Later driving alternators only, it was scrapped when, in 1958 current was taken from the Grid.

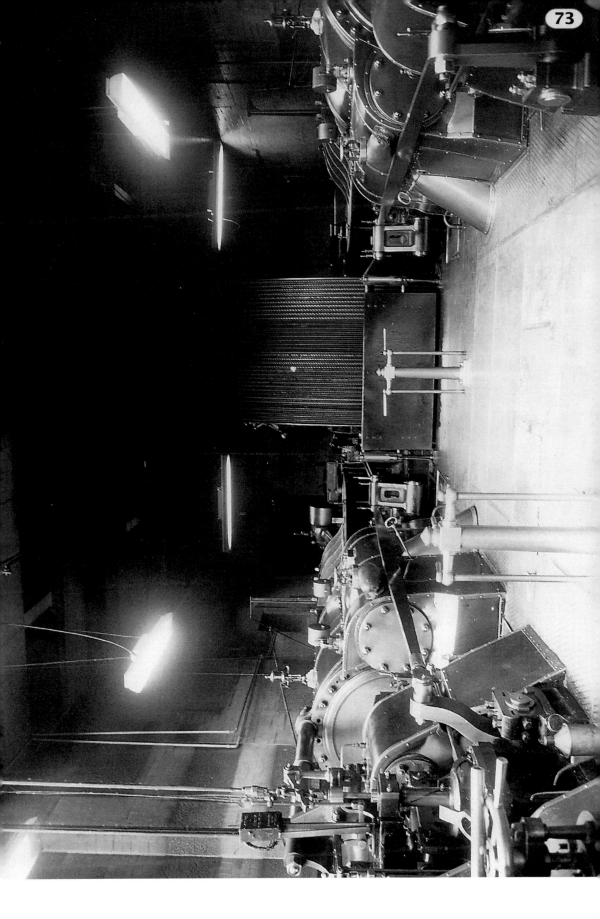

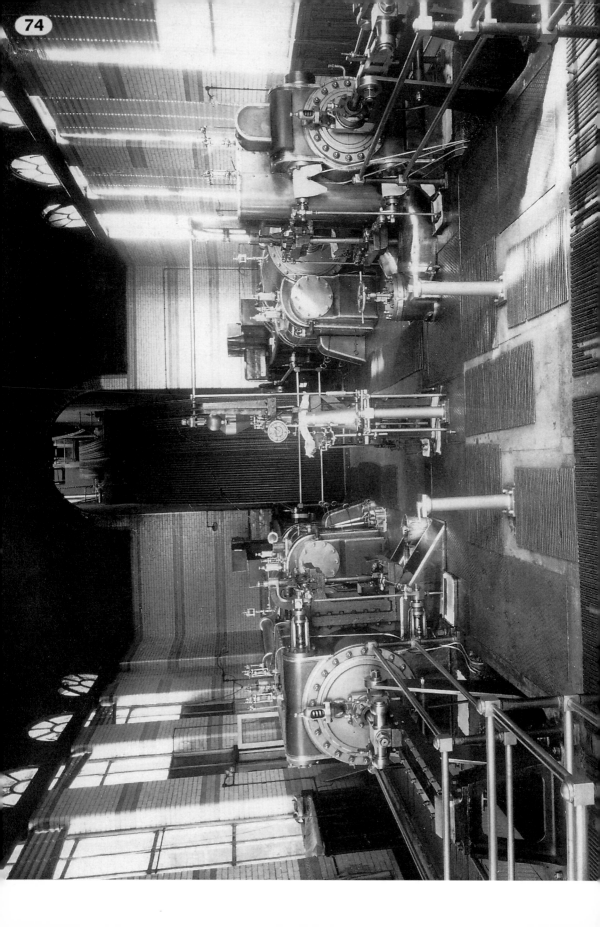

The coarse-count spinning trade of Oldham required great power, and this was best provided by a massive but simple engine. Buckley & Taylor built many beam engines for this trade (nos 11-13), turning later to the horizontal and vertical types.

BUCKLEY AND TAYLOR, CASTLE IRONWORKS, OLDHAM

76 Commercial Mill, Oldham.

Cotton Spinning

The mill was built in 1873, with a double beam engine and gear drive, but the engines were completely wrecked, with the loss of two lives, when the flywheel burst in 1889. The directors decided to continue with a new power system, and no 76, Buckley & Taylor's standard design, of which they had supplied many, was running in eight months, in the new engine house. Called 'Patience' and 'Perseverance', it was a twin tandem compound with slide-valve cylinders 21 and 42in bore by 5ft stroke, which supplied with steam at 100psi, developed 1,200hp at 60rpm. The drive was by 24 ropes from the 26ft flywheel. Closed in World War II, the mill was re-opened in 1954, but closed again in 1959. The makers built some thirty engines of this design, all with slide-valves, but this was the last to remain unaltered; most had Corliss high-pressure cylinders and higher-pressure boilers fitted in the early 1900s.

77 Unity Ring Mill, Heywood, Lancs.

Cotton Spinning

Illustrating the next phase in Buckley & Taylor's design, this was built in 1909, although they were making vertical engines before then. The Corliss-valve cylinders were 20 and 41in bore by 5ft stroke, which with steam at 160psi developed 1,900hp at 67rpm. The high-pressure cylinders are still at the rear, with the air pumps driven from the crossheads, but it was governed by cut-off of the Corliss-valves, in contrast to no 76 which to the end was throttle controlled. It ran with very little trouble until the mill was closed in 1958. The 24ft flywheel weighed 53tons.

78 Lilac Mill, Shaw, Nr Oldham, Lancs.

Cotton Spinning

Lilac illustrates the last phase of Buckley & Taylor tandems, as it was a triple expansion with all Corliss-valves. The mill was planned in 1914, but due to World War I it did not start working until 1922. The engine was large even by Lancashire standards, with cylinders 28, 42, 47, and 47in bore by 5ft stroke, which developed 2,500hp at 66rpm with steam at 180psi. Grooved for 48 ropes, the flywheel was 24ft diameter. The boilers were later converted to pulverised coal firing, but all was scrapped in 1955, on the change to electric drives. Contrasting with the previous two Buckley & Taylors, it will be noted that the air pumps and condensers are now at the rear.

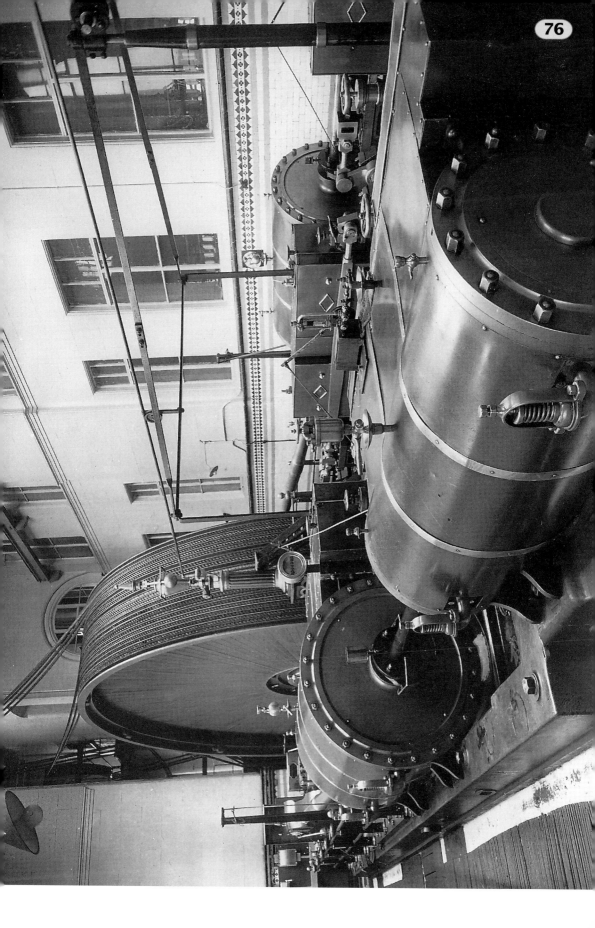

Acknowledgements

So many have contributed to the records that acknowledgements can only be general so I express my grateful thanks to:

The engineers and managers everywhere whose friendliness and help made the record possible. Shown in their everyday work, the condition of the engines is tribute to the devoted care they received.

Frank Wightman of Stretford, whose incredible knowledge of mills and engines, and more so of their positions, has ever been at my disposal.

Mr Harold Bottoms, who as chief engineer of the Lancashire Cotton Corporation when they owned more mill engines than any other group, ensured that I should see them all, hence their frequent appearance in the record. My meetings with him and Mr Harrop were highlights of my Lancashire visits.

Mr Vincent Taylor of Combined English Mills who, equally kind regarding their many engines, added much to my debt by the present of Skinners Cotton Trade Directory for 1925-6, a superb record of the trade at its peak.

The fitters, engineers, and millwrights, especially Messrs Wainwright of Staleybridge and Brown Son & Pickles, particularly the late Johnny Pickles himself. Always busy, they found time to talk of engines with me and tell of repairs and alterations in mill power plant. This often led to changes of plans to include the unusual, generally with their blessing of personal reference to the engineers and managers.

All assisted when much material was lost, by replacing missing data. This greatly reduced errors, but many remain despite every effort. Ever inquiring 'When are you going to write a book about engines?' they kept in mind the need for a project to record engineering at its best, but sheer lack of opportunity prevented this.

So to Bath University of Technology, and Dr Buchanan, my deepest thanks are due for providing the facilities and encouragement to prepare the material for publication. Without this, the whole must have remained unused.

To make the story more complete, I have included certain examples which are not from my own collection, and I am grateful to the editors of *The Engineer* and *Engineering* for permission to use illustrations from those journals.

ENGINE TYPES

Beam Engines

Vertical Engines

Hoirizontal Engincs

Simple Expansion

Single Tandem Compound Slide valves

Corliss-and slide-valves

Corliss-valves

Drop valves

Twin Tandem Compound

Ross Mill, Bacup, (Yates & Thom, 1914-21)	58
Hartford Mill, Oldham, (Urmson & Thompson, 1907)	59
Lion Mill, Royton, (Pollitt & Wigzell, 1890)	60
State Mill, Rochdale, (J. & W. McNaught, 1901)	61
Dee Mill, Shaw, (Scott & Hodgson, 1907)	62
Broadbents, Droylsden, (Woolstenholme & Rye, 1878)	70-72
R. Shackleton, Rochdale, (Petrie, 1909)	75
Commercial Mill, Oldham, (Buckley & Taylor, 1889)	76
Unity Ring Mill, Heywood, (Buckley & Taylor, 1909)	77

Twin Tandem Triple Expansion

Perseverance Mill, Padiham, (Burnley Iron Works, 1906)	63
Wilton Mill, Radcliffe, (Galloways, 1907)	64
Ashton Bros, Hyde, (Goodfellows, 1895)	65
Rock Mill, Ashton, (G. Saxon, 1892)	66
Imperial Mill, Blackburn, (Yates & Thom, 1901)	67
Eclipse Mill, Rochdale, (McNaught, 1900)	68
Trencherfield Mill, Wigan, (J. & E. Wood, 1907)	69
Brierfield Mill, Brierfield, (Petrie, 1898)	73
Era Mill, Rochdale, (Petrie, 1898)	74
Lilac Mill, Shaw, (Buckley & Taylor, 1914)	78

MAKERS

(numbers relate to plates)

Ashton & Frost, Blackburn,	40
Bagshaw, J., Barley,	22
Bates, T., Sowerby Bridge,	3, 10
Bowling Ironworks, Bradford,	4
Bracewell, Wm., Burnley,	8, 15
Buckley & Taylor, Oldham,	11, 12, 13,16, 76, 77, 78
Burnley Ironworks, Burnley,	63
Carels, Ghent, Belgium,	54
Carmichael, Dundee,	45
Cole,	5
Cole, Marchent & Morley, Bradford,	47, 56
Douglas & Grant, Kirkaldy,	57
Earnshaw & Holt, Rochdale,	28
Ebor Engineering Co, Littleborough,	37
Fairbairn, Wm., Manchester,	23
Galloway, W. & J., Manchester,	64
Goodfellow, Benj., Hyde,	7, 35, 65
Hick, Benj., Bolton,	6, 14
Hick, Hargreaves,	49
Leigh, Evan,	21
Lees, T. & R., Hollinwood,	29
Low Moor Ironworks, Bradford,	9
Marsdens Engines, Heckmondwyke,	48
McNaught, J. & W., Rochdale,	34, 38, 61, 68
Musgrave & Sons, J., Bolton,	30, 50, 52
Pollitt & Wigzell, Sowerby Bridge,	32, 55, 60
Petrie, John & Co, Rochdale,	2, 17, 73,74, 75
Roberts, Wm., Nelson,	42
Robinson, J., Manchester,	44
Saxon, Geo., Manchester,	66
Schofield & Taylor, Huddersfield,	27
Scott & Hodgson, Guide Bridge,	20, 39, 62
Stott, S. S. & Son, Haslingden,	18, 43
Thompson, J., Colne,	19
Thomson, J. & G., Clydebank,	24
Urmson & Thompson,	59
Whittaker, C., Haslingden,	41
Wood, Baldwin, Brighouse,	31
Wood Bros, Sowerby Bridge,	25
Wood, John & Edward, Bolton,	51, 59
Woodhouse & Mitchell, Brighouse,	46
Woolstenholme & Rye, Oldham,	70, 71, 72
Yates, W. & J., Blackburn,	36
Yates & Thom, Blackburn,	53, 58, 67
Unknown,	1, 26

The Textile Mill Engine

Part 2

Beehive Mill, Bolton, Lances, *see page 4*

Bliss Mill, Chipping Norton, *see page 4*

— Contents —

Inverted Vertical Engines

Introduction

Following the pattern of part 1, this second part begins with a broad review of how individual mill power plants developed, and then considers the types which drove the mills of the last great expansion period of the early twentieth century, with brief notes on engines made outside the textile counties, and some less used types. Notes on boilers follow, the whole being rounded off by considering how the power was transmitted, with brief sections devoted to the mills themselves and to the engine men and their works. Sheer lack of space has meant that treatment is greatly condensed, and much material prepared has had to be cut out; this will explain omissions obvious to anyone familiar with the mill scene. However, the curtailment is not without virtue, since it has resulted in compact and easily handled Parts.

The evolution of mill power plants was as varied as the engines and mills themselves. Thus many mills such as the *Iris* (part 1 No 11) ran their whole life with the original engines modernised, regularly paying good dividends. *Commercial*, which was not far away, was built with a similar power plant and drive, but the engine was completely wrecked about twenty years later. As the mill was little damaged, a new engine room and drives were installed, and this ran until the mill closed in 1954 (See part 1 No 76.). Salts, of Saltaire, Yorkshire, had a very different story. This was a large mill built in 1850, and provided with a powerful Fairbairn double beam drop-valve engine with cylinders 50in bore by 7ft stroke in each half. One of the Salt sons, George, was an accomplished engineer, and under his guidance, when Corliss-valves were introduced, cylinders of this type replaced the original ones. Soon after, a vertical single cylinder Corliss engine was installed to drive one of the vertical shafts of the front mills, to be followed in 1872 by a horizontal single Corliss engine 30in bore by 8ft stroke, which drove the rear combing and weaving sheds by 24in belts whose silence was much appreciated. Two very large Galloway boilers, 12ft diameter by 20ft long, aided the Cornish multitubular boilers of 1850. In 1892 the power plant was brought up to date by the installation of a 500hp inverted vertical Corliss engine with rope drives in each of the front sections of the mills, two horizontal tandems for the combing and weaving, and two small pumping engines. All steamed by six new boilers, this gave efficient service until electric driving was installed when, with two turbine generators replacing six engines, the power system reverted to two units as in 1850.

Crossleys of Halifax differed again, since starting with one small mill, others were added as the business grew so that by 1865 there were several mills all with simple expansion beam engines. Crossleys, too, were blessed with a family engineer and good staff, so in the 1860s, the beam engines were McNaught compounded and steamed by several batteries of the newly invented Howards water-tube boilers. With the development of horizontal engines, there followed a large Pollitts tandem in 1872, and this set the pattern for compound engines and higher pressures for fifty years, until the 1920s led to the installation of steam turbines and electric driving. Listers of Manningham, Bradford, had a similar story. Here the mills, rebuilt in 1870-72, possessed seven engines by 1882, including a double beam of 1,000hp. All of them were replaced by high-pressure compounds in later years, these again succumbing to a central turbine electric power plant in the 1930s. Cotton mills were usually planned as large central units, but there were also those which grew piecemeal like the Yorkshire concerns just noted, and where it later paid to install one large engine, driving the sections by ropes or shafts. Scott & Hodgson specialised in schemes of this type. Thus at the Oxford Mills, Ashton under Lyne, there were three mill blocks each with its own engine, and about 1905, Scotts fitted a fine vertical triple expansion engine which drove all three sections by shafts over the yard. Again, by 1888, A. & A. Crompton at Shaw drove several blocks by two beam and one horizontal engines, and J. & E. Wood then fitted the largest compound engine that they built, 2,000hp with cylinders 36 and 66in bore by 6ft stroke, to drive the whole by ropes. The same company's adjacent Woodside mill later had its own vertical triple expansion engine and in 1931 the two engines were replaced by a Richardson Westgarth steam turbine which drove one mill by ropes and the other from an alternator.

Robert Hyde Buckley also installed a similar scheme in the 1930s when they replaced three Goodfellows engines, each with gear drives, by a Daniel Adamson turbine which drove two sections by ropes, and the third by an alternator. These were adaptations to give the older mills the economy of the later ones, but *Elk*, the last steam spinning mill to be built (Part 2 No 66) was designed to work in this manner. The woolcombing mill of Yorkshire usually comprised a single-floor building with a single heavy mainshaft, from which the machines were driven. Isaac Holdens at Bradford (1883) was a remarkable instance of this with six mainshafts each running one half of the length, ie three running from each end. Each shaft was rope driven by its own 300hp horizontal single-cylinder Hick Hargreaves Corliss engine, so that in a house at each end there were three engines each driving a single shaft by ropes. All were tandem compounded about twenty years later, running thus until the whole was replaced by a turbine generator supplying current to drive each shaft by a motor. Ashworth, Hadwens at Droylsden was one of the first mills to replace mechanical by electric drive. Built in 1840 it had a 1,000hp beam engine which ran at 23rpm, the power being transmitted through 99 pairs of bevel wheels, and the whole of this was replaced about 1907 by a turbo alternator, with motors in various departments; the spinning mill had one motor driving each two floors by ropes.

Acknowledgements

The prints and the information upon the engines are their own tribute to the engineers and managers who were so helpful everywhere. I am grateful to the editor of *Engineering* for leave to include plates 59, 60 and 61, adding much to the value of these sections. To Frank Wightman for specially preparing plates 69 and 70, and as always providing a maximum of information in a minimum of space. To the now unknown donors of a Carmichael's catalogue for No 62A and B, and copies for plates No 63A and B, delightful examples of Scottish craftsmanship which I could not resist including. I thank them all for making the volume possible.

(continued from Part 1)

A small number of horizontal triple-expansion engines were built with single low-pressure cylinders, which made a compact and economical engine suitable for the smaller power needed in the weaving sheds.

1 J. Sunderland & Co, Oakbank Mill, Nelson, Lancs.

Cotton Weaving

This was built by Pollitt & Wigzell in 1897 to develop 500hp at 70rpm, using steam at 150psi. The Corliss-valve high-and intermediate-pressure cylinders, of 18 and 26in bore, drove the left-hand crank, with the 42in bore slide-valve low-pressure and the condenser behind on the right-hand side, all of 4ft stroke. Driving by twelve ropes from the 18ft flywheel, it was supplying more than the designed power to drive over 1,100 looms in later years, but by 1966, with the installation of electric drives the engine was scrapped.

2 The Hendon Room & Power Co, Hendon Shed, Nelson.

Cotton Weaving

Hendon was next to Oakbank Mill, and was fitted with 'Nora', a similar engine made by Wm Roberts & Co, Phoenix Foundry, Nelson in 1900. Designed to develop 500hp, the cylinders were Corliss high and intermediate of $14\frac{1}{2}$ and $21\frac{1}{4}$in bore on the right-hand side, with the $36\frac{1}{2}$in bore low-pressure again with slide-valve and condenser behind on the left-hand crank. Running at 76rpm, it drove by thirteen ropes from the 16ft flywheel, supplying power to small groups of weavers who shared the premises, and sometimes needed 700hp. The process steam load was heavy since the yarn was size coated on the premises, and two boilers were used until, when the mill closed in 1960, all of the plant was scrapped.

3 The Oldham Velvet Co, Falcon Mill, Oldham.

Velvet Weaving

Renowned as a cotton spinning town, Oldham also had a small weaving industry, and the Falcon shed had a three-cylinder horizontal triple-expansion engine. Built in 1885, probably by Buckley & Taylor, little was known of its history, except that it was originally a slide-valve compound with cylinders about 18 and 30in bore by 4ft stroke using steam at 100psi. It was converted to triple-expansion in 1910 by Urmson & Thompson, who supplied the Corliss-valve high-pressure cylinder, and altered it to make a triple of 13, 21, and 30in bore, with the original 4ft stroke and gear drive unaltered. It ran thus with a new boiler for 150psi, until, on the closure of the mill in 1957, all was scrapped.

2

NORA

Three examples of this simple type which long gave economical service in the weaving sheds, where a reliable engine was essential.

4 G. Whittle & Co, Stonebridge Mills, Longridge, Nr Preston.

Cotton Weaving

Beginning with one shed driven by a single beam engine, the business grew so that, in 1877, a further large shed was built, and this engine was provided to drive the whole. Made by Joseph Clayton & Co, Preston, who also supplied the two boilers, this power plant ran unaltered, and years later also drove another shed, so developing more than the designed 350hp. The cylinders were 18 and 32in bore by 4ft 6in stroke, with cross cut-off valves fitted to the high-pressure cylinder, under the control of the governor on the right-hand side of the engine, with an overriding throttle valve worked by the governor on the left-hand side. The whole ran with little trouble until 1956 when, with the pressure on the original boilers reduced to 50psi, and new boilers too costly, the mill was closed and all was scrapped, except the newer looms which were sold to Africa. Running at 48rpm, it drove by teeth on the 15ft diameter flywheel rim to a 6ft 6in pinion on the shed shaft. The original timber covering over the flywheel teeth remained to the end.

5 The Jubilee Room & Power Co, Padiham, Lancs.

Cotton Weaving

Built as Progress Mill for J. Roberts in 1888 with a single shed, sufficient power was provided to drive two. The engine was made by W. & J. Yates of Blackburn, fitted with cylinders of 21 and 42in bore by 5ft stroke, again with cross cut-off valves on the high-pressure cylinder, but with the overspeed control combined in a single governor. The drive was by a gear ring on the flywheel arms, and when the new shed was added in 1906, it was driven by bevel gears from the original second motion shaft. The full 600hp was then required, and the engine ran at 56rpm, the steam being supplied at 140psi, at first by two three-flued boilers by W. & J. Yates, which were replaced by three twin-flue boilers by Yates & Thom in 1906. It still ran perfectly at eighty years old, well kept and most attractive with its original wooden lagging.

6 The Hollinbank Room & Power Co, Brierfield, Nr Burnley, Lancs.

Cotton Weaving

Typical of Wm Roberts' early design, 'Edith' and 'Clara' was built in 1892, to develop 1,000hp. Designed for rope drive, the speed of 70rpm was higher, and the whole lighter, than the gear-drive plants. The cylinders were $22^1/_2$ and 45in bore by 5ft stroke and it remained unaltered, retaining the high-pressure valve chest on the outer side of the cylinder (characteristic of Roberts' early practice) with cross cut-off valves under governor control. The drive was by eighteen ropes from the 20ft flywheel, with 32 bevel-wheel driven cross shafts for the looms. A single boiler drove the first part erected in 1892, others being added in 1898 and 1902 as the shed was completed to the original plan, all being scrapped when the plant was closed about 1963.

6

Cross Compound Corliss-Valves

Three examples which illustrate the highly economical engines developed for smaller powers in later years.

7 Lawrence Cotton Ltd, Fernhurst Mill, Blackburn.

Cotton Weaving

Built by Clayton & Goodfellows of Blackburn in 1908, this was their works Nos 540 and 541 and typical of their medium-sized engines. The Corliss-valve high-pressure cylinder was 16in bore and the 30in bore low pressure had a slide valve, with the boiler feed pump driven from the valve tail rod, a good practice rarely met outside the Blackburn area. Using steam at 160psi from a single boiler, it developed 400hp at 60rpm for over fifty years. The drive was by fourteen ropes, and the high-pressure trip motion was the makers' patent, in which the dies, receding as they tripped, had a life of up to twenty years un-changed. The engine was scrapped when electric drives were installed.

8 The Jacquard Weaving Co, Sunnybank Mill, Kirkham, Lancs.

Cotton Weaving

'Progress' and 'Perseverance' was supplied by J. Foster & Sons, Preston, for the Room & Power Co who built the shed in 1907. Typical of Fosters' shed engines, it was the last one at work, giving nearly fifty years' service before the conversion to motor driving. The Corliss-valve cylinders were 17 and 34in bore by 4ft 6in stroke, and it developed 450hp at 80rpm using steam at 175psi from a boiler also made by Fosters. Driving by sixteen ropes from the 18-ton 18ft flywheel, little repair was ever needed.

9 J. Butterworth & Co, Dale Mill, Waterfoot, Haslingden.

Cotton Spinning and Weaving

Built by S. S. Stott & Co, Haslingden, in 1911, this replaced a double beam engine in the same room. The cylinders were 17 and 35in bore by 4ft stroke, and it developed 450hp on steam at 160psi for some forty-five years until electric drives were installed. 'Agnes' and 'Amy' drove by gearing to the original second motion shaft, but in 1911, the drives to the mill room shafts were converted from gearing to ropes; one drive can be seen at the right.

Examples illustrating three makers' practice in large spinning mill engine building.

10 The Lancashire Cotton Corporation, Manor Mill, Hollinwood.

Cotton Spinning

One of Geo Saxons' many fine engines, this had two unusual features: the piston tail rods were encased in tubes, and the rear cylinder head nuts and studs were covered by a raised lagging ring (they were usually left bare as in Nos 8 and 9, or else the whole was covered as in Nos 11 and 12). Built in 1907 to develop 1,200hp, the cylinders were 25 and 52in bore by 5ft stroke, using steam at 160psi, and running at $64^1/_2$rpm. Originally driving the mill floors by 28 ropes from the 26ft flywheel, much of the load in later years was driving an alternator, supplying the ring frame motors, all being scrapped when the mill was closed in 1963.

11 The Lancashire Cotton Corporation, Hawk Mill, Shaw.

Cotton Spinning

The mill was built in 1908, and the engine supplying 1,500hp was made by Yates & Thom, Blackburn. The cylinders were $27^3/_4$ and 56in bore by 5ft stroke, and it ran at 70rpm, using steam at 175psi, driving by 37 ropes from the 22ft flywheel. In contrast to No 10, Yates & Thom preferred a trunk-type frame, which together with the valve gear and flat tail rod slides, were characteristic of the makers' design. All was scrapped about 1964.

12 Horrocks, Crewdson & Co, Preston.

Cotton Spinning

'King' and 'Queen'was built by Hick Hargreaves, Bolton, in 1915, and was works No 715. Designed to develop 2,000hp, the cylinders were 30 and 60in bore by 5ft stroke, running at 65rpm, and using steam at 180psi. The 46-rope drive from the 25ft flywheel was split; most of the ropes went forward to the millshaft, those driving to the rear were for an alternator supplying motors in another section. Widespread use of Grid current, and motor drives in later years led to the scrapping of the several engines, but the concern stopped producing in the early 1960s after 150 years in business.

Three examples of engines made and used in Lancashire, which were almost certainly the largest engines that these concerns built.

13 The Lancashire Cotton Corporation, May Mill, Pemberton, Wigan.

Cotton Spinning

The May engine built by Ashton Frost of Blackburn in 1902, was one of the few spinning-mill engines they constructed. Designed to develop 1,500hp at 62rpm, the cylinders were $23^3/_4$ and $50^1/_2$in bore by 5ft stroke, driving by 34 $1^1/_2$in ropes from the 28ft flywheel. Three boilers by Musgraves, Bolton, supplied steam originally at 200psi, and 180psi in 1957. Conversion of the mill to electric ring spinning frames proceeded from 1960, and was completed by 1962, the engine being scrapped in 1964.

14 The Facit Mill Co, Facit, Nr Rochdale.

Cotton Spinning

Made by J. & W. McNaught in 1905, 'Facit' was their works No 1042, designed to develop 2,000hp. The cylinders were 27 and 57in bore by 5ft stroke, the low-pressure certainly being the largest cylinder of its design that they made. The drive was by 30 ropes from a 24ft flywheel, and the mill was interesting in that, since it was built in a narrow valley, there was little room for the usual condenser cooling pond, which was therefore placed partly beneath the mill itself. The plant gave good service until 1958, when electric driving was installed, one of the motors being seen in the rope race driving to the room shaft by vee belts.

15 The Wye Mill Co, No 2 Mill, Shaw, Lancashire.

Cotton Spinning (1926)

Wye No 2 was significant in that not only was it the last spinning mill to be built with the traditional engine and rope drives, but it was also the last and the largest mill engine the makers, Buckley & Taylor, Oldham, built. Designed to develop 2,500hp, the cylinders were 32 and 70in bore by 5ft stroke, the low-pressure cylinder being the third largest in a Lancashire spinning mill (Sun Mill low-pressure was 73in and Mons was $72^1/_4$in bore). Running at 66rpm, it used steam at 180psi, and until 1960 all of the power was delivered to the mill floors by 48 ropes from the 24ft flywheel. Then with the introduction of motor-driven ring spinning frames, the engine was used to drive these through an alternator, but by 1964 Grid current was cheaper and the engine was then stopped. The photograph was taken in the early 1950s, when the two Kenyon's ropers seen in front of the flywheel had fitted the 19 new ropes seen (lighter colour) on the right-hand side.

Three examples to illustrate large engine construction east of the Pennines.

16 Timothy Hird & Company, Knowle Mill, Keighley.

Woollen Spinning

Another instance of a builder's last and largest engine, this was made by Marsdens Engines, of Heckmondwyke, in 1926, to replace the original engine when the mill was doubled in size. 'Richard' and 'Sarah' was fitted with cylinders of 22 and 44in bore by 4ft 6in stroke, developed 1,000hp at 75rpm when using steam at 160psi, and originally drove all the machinery through ropes. The introduction of electric machinery led to the installation of a 600hp alternator in 1952, but later association with a new group led to the use of Grid current only and the engine was scrapped. Two boilers by Hewett & Kellet supplied the steam. The original engine at the mill was a Musgrave's tandem.

17 Oates Brothers, Ryburn Mills, Halifax.

Woollen Spinning

Built by Pollitt & Wigzell in 1921, 'Edwin' and 'Emmie' replaced a 250 and a 300hp engine and drove the new extension then built, by motors and an alternator. Developing 1,200hp at 70rpm, the cylinders were 23 and 45in bore by 5ft stroke, using steam at 160psi, and in 42 years of work, much of it day and night, only one Corliss-valve was replaced. Much of the plant was driven directly by ropes and shafting, as was the 300hp alternator, but from 1963, the gradual installation of electric drives, due to be completed by 1966, superseded the engine, which was scrapped.

18 Holmes, Mann & Company, Harris Street, Bradford.

Woolcombing, then sawmill

The premises were built for H. D. Shaw & Company, woolcombers, in 1921, and the engine made by Newton, Bean & Mitchell was then installed new. The cylinders were 20 and 40in bore by 2ft 6in stroke, developing about 650hp at l00rpm, with steam at 120psi. Drop-piston inlet-valves fitted at the top with horizontal piston exhaust valves at the bottom controlled the steam, with the condenser on the right, driven from the highpressure piston tail rod. Originally the customary single woolcomber's shaft was driven by 12 ropes. This drive was retained on the change to sawmilling, but then arranged to drive an alternator, the machines being motor-driven. The flywheel diameter was 15ft.

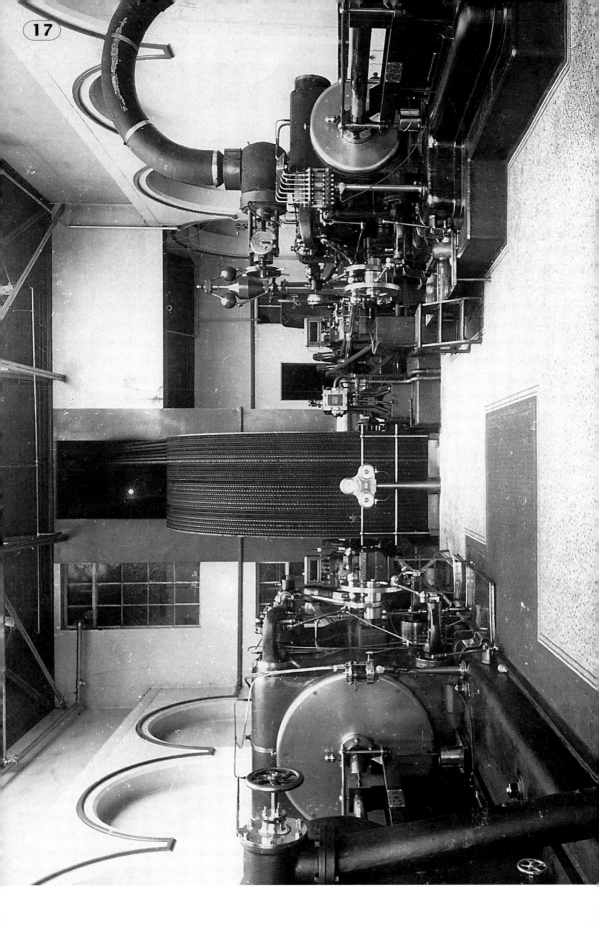

Cross Compounds with Valves Below

Most Corliss-valve engines were constructed with the steam valves at the top and the exhausts below, but all of the valves were sometimes placed at the bottom as the following examples indicate.

19 The Mutual Mills Co, Heywood, No 1 Mill.

Cotton Spinning

For the first two of the four mills which they eventually built (No 2 was triple-expansion, 1893), Mutual chose engines built by J. & E. Wood of Bolton, who regularly placed the valves below. Called 'Hornby' and 'Tattersall', it was a cross compound designed to develop about 1,250hp at 53rpm, using steam at 100psi with cylinders 30 and 53in bore by 6ft stroke. Built in 1885, it was a typical Woods' design of the period, with horizontal single-cylinder barring engine, the main steam valve placed inside of the high-pressure valve gear, and a high engine centre line. Little but the governor was altered in over 65 years of work, the only major expenditure being for new valve gear in 1913, and ports rebored and new valves fitted in 1952. The 35-rope drive from the 28ft flywheel gave little trouble until all was scrapped when electric driving was installed later.

20 Marsden Mills, Nelson, Lancs.

Cotton Weaving

Marsden was one of the later plants containing two Burnley Ironworks engines of 1908 and 1912 for the two sections, which contained over 1,500 looms in each. Only the 1912 engine had the valves below, and was typical of the makers' late design. The cylinders were 22 and 44in bore by 4ft 6in stroke, developing over 800hp at 80rpm with steam at 160psi. Four boilers between the engines supplied steam; one of them was added when the later engine was installed. All was scrapped when the premises went into other occupancy in the 1950s. It was probable that no rope was ever changed in 45 years.

21 The Slack Mills Co, Hyde, Cheshire.

Cotton Spinning and Weaving

When Daniel Adamson took up a licence to build Wheelock engines in the UK the Slack Mills fitted one in each of their four mills, and 'Margaret', the last of these, was fitted to drive the weaving shed in 1889. Developing 500hp with steam at 120psi, the cylinders were 20 and 38in bore by 4ft 6in stroke, and she ran at 62rpm. The high-pressure cylinder was fitted with the type 'A' valve gear with twin plugs, with the steam inlets in the middle, the low-pressure containing the simpler semi-rotating slide-valves, also below. Although a typically light American design, she was completely unaltered after seventy years of hard work, when the engines were scrapped and electric motors were installed. The drive was by a separate gear wheel staked on to the crankshaft; this wheel, with 111 teeth 13in wide, drove to the 57-toothed pinion on the weaving shed shaft.

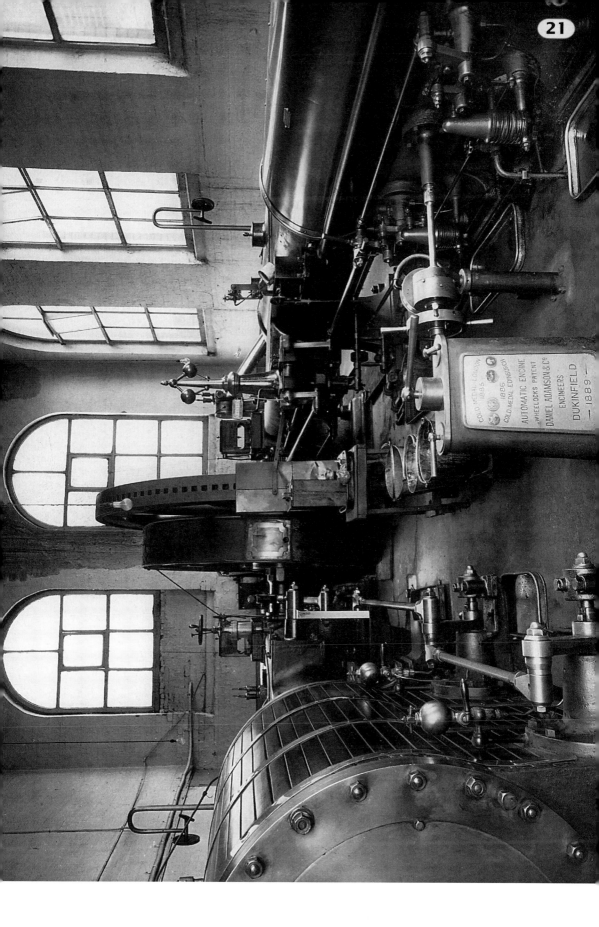

Drop-valves were long used on beam engines, but were eclipsed by the economy of Corliss-valves in later years. There was, however, a return to the use of the drop-valves at the turn of the nineteenth century. They were suitable for high superheat, and when repeated tests on the Continent gave good economy, they were soon adopted for mill engines by the Lancashire engine builders.

22 The Hollins Mill Co, Marple, Cheshire.

Cotton Spinning and Weaving

In their many years in business, Hollins made every effort to secure the highest economy, and in later years used a 750hp Westinghouse vertical three-crank gas engine to power the spinning mill. In 1922, however, a major re-organisation was effected, in which the whole of the power was taken from a single large engine, and 'Peace' and 'Plenty' was provided by Scott & Hodgsons to do this job. Developing 1,800hp from cylinders 26 and 56in bore by 5ft stroke, it was works No 658 (works numbers were rare on Scott's engines) and used steam at 180psi. Built to drive by 30 ropes from the 25ft flywheel, it was later altered to drive by several steel belts, and was the last of several such spinning mill drives to remain, but everything was scrapped when the mill closed about 1956.

23 Mutual Mills, Heywood, No 3 Mill.

Cotton Spinning

When Mutual decided to build their No 3 Mill in 1914, J. & E. Wood had closed, and so could not repeat their successful engines of the No 1 and 2 mills (see No 19); therefore the order was given to Hick Hargreaves who tendered for the 1,850hp engine for £4,000. Due to the 1914-18 War, the mill and engine were not completed until 1923, and the price was adjusted. Three 30ft by 9ft boilers were supplied, with superheaters, in 1918, working at 160psi. It was highly economical and an interesting feature was the racks and pinions provided to traverse the rear cylinder covers during repairs. The No 4 mill was built for electric drive.

24 The Grape Mill Co, Royton, Lancs.

Cotton Spinning

Musgrave of Bolton adopted the drop-piston valve, and in 1904 engaged Mr Steiger of Switzerland to design the engines. They were very successful, and Grape and the smaller engine of the type at a Burnley weaving shed were said to be the most economical in Lancashire. Built in 1905 to develop 2,000hp at 80rpm, the Grape engine had cylinders of $29^1/_2$ and 60in bore by 5ft stroke and used superheated steam at 160psi from four of the five boilers. The flywheel with the arm boarding splayed out to meet the rim was a Musgrave's feature, the drive from the 24ft rim being by 44 ropes. Bad coal and smoke led to the fitting of mechanical stokers in 1957, but the mill was closed in 1960.

Three examples to illustrate other aspects of the drop-valve engine.

25 Samuel Lomax & Co, Radcliffe, Lancs.

Textile Finishing

Another example of Continental design made in England, this was purchased second-hand from a margarine factory in 1923. Made by Jessop & Son, Leicester, about 1902, it was fitted with Collmann's valve gear, a special feature of which was that a single leaf spring was used to return both inlet valves to their seats. Developing about 350hp at 80rpm, the cylinders were 16 and 30in bore by 3ft 6in stroke. Two Tinker Shenton's boilers fitted new in 1923, supplied steam for this, another engine, and the process steam load until the mill was closed and all scrapped in 1960.

26 The Lancashire Cotton Corporation, Mons Mill, Todmorden.

Cotton Spinning

An example of an engine designed and built on the Continent, Mons was the largest of six or seven Carels' engines installed in Lancashire cotton mills. It was designed to develop 3,000hp (required, had the Hare Spinning Co for whom it was built completed the second mill) with cylinders $39\frac{1}{2}$ and $72\frac{1}{4}$in bore by 4ft $7\frac{3}{4}$ in stroke, running at 80rpm. Designed to use steam at 200psi, needed to drive the double mill, it usually ran on 160psi, for the single mill completed. Five boilers were installed, with room for two more for the whole scheme. The 24ft diameter flywheel, made in three sections, was 13ft 8in wide, for 69 ropes, and weighed 130 tons with crankshaft. Motor-driven ring spinning frames were gradually installed, and the engine was dismantled when this was completed in 1964, but the mill was closed in 1968. The low-pressure cylinder was the second largest in Lancashire.

27 Thomas Melland & Sons, Elm St, Burnley.

Cotton Weaving

This was an interesting engine. It was almost certainly the last new engine supplied to a cotton weaving shed, and the only cross compound built by Galloways for the extraction of process steam between the high-and low-pressure cylinders. The business, started in 1895, began weaving in 1900. The original engine, probably made by Roberts of Nelson, was seriously damaged by fire in 1926, and the Galloway was designed to fit the same space and drives. The cylinders were 21 and 38in bore by 3ft stroke, developing 600hp at 125rpm, and, called 'Brian' and 'David', it cost £8,000, and gave every satisfaction until the business was closed forty years later. It is a tribute to Tinker Shenton's who made the boilers in 1900, that they supplied steam at the original 150psi, for each of the engines, ie over 65 years. A fine example of a late Lancashire mill engine, this will be preserved for re-erection at Manchester University.

Inverted Vertical Triple Expansion

This was a late phase in the evolution of engine design, which, as it was lighter and ran at higher speed, was less costly to install.

28 The Lancashire Cotton Corporation, Malta Mill, Middleton, Lancs.

Cotton Spinning

Malta was a typical Buckley & Taylor's triple, in which the crankshaft bearing sockets were cast with the bedplate, the cylinders entirely separate, and the Corliss-valves all in line with the crankshaft, the whole being tied together by a massive entablature on the top of the columns. Built in 1904, the cylinders were 23, 34, and 56in bore by 4ft stroke, developing 1,600hp at 71 rpm. Three Tetlow's boilers for 185psi were installed, and another by Oldham Boiler Works added in 1914. The flywheel was 22ft diameter, weighed 45 tons and drove by 32 ropes. The whole ran for nearly sixty years without alteration and with little repair until the mill closed in 1963, when all was scrapped.

29 The Arrow Mill, Castleton, Rochdale.

Cotton Spinning

Arrow, containing five acres of floor space, was an example of the speed of mill building at the time. The contract to build was signed late in 1906, the first brick was laid in January 1907, the engine first ran under steam in February 1908, and the first cotton was spun in this large mill fifteen months after the first brick was laid. One of the only two vertical triples which J. & W. McNaught of Rochdale made, 'Reliance' was designed to develop 1,700hp at 75rpm. The Corliss-valve high-and intermediate-pressure cylinders were 25 and 38in bore, and as often in Rochdale practice, the 60in low-pressure was fitted with a piston valve. The 22ft flywheel drove by 40 ropes and the barring engine with its horizontal cylinder driving through a vertical crankshaft was a typical McNaught feature. Four boilers by Tinker Shenton supplied steam at 180psi until some fifty years later the mill was converted to electric drive from the Grid and the engine was scrapped.

30 The Crest Mill, Castleton, Rochdale.

Cotton Spinning

J Petrie of Rochdale only made three vertical triple-expansion engines, which went to the Crest and Marland mills at Rochdale, and the Linnet at Gee Cross. Crest Mill was built in 1907 for ring spinning, and needed only two floors to use the 1,800hp that 'Gladys', the engine, developed. The high-pressure cylinder, 21in bore, had Corliss-valves across the cylinder centre line, whilst the intermediate-and low-pressures, each fitted with piston valves, were 34 and 56in bore, all by 4ft stroke. Running at 75rpm, it drove by 32 ropes from the 26ft flywheel. Steam was supplied by four Yates & Thom boilers, 9ft in diameter, at 190psi which had to be maintained for full load, when up to 120 tons of coal were used per week. The mill was later converted to electric drive, and the engine scrapped. The high-pressure crank was a half or single web type.

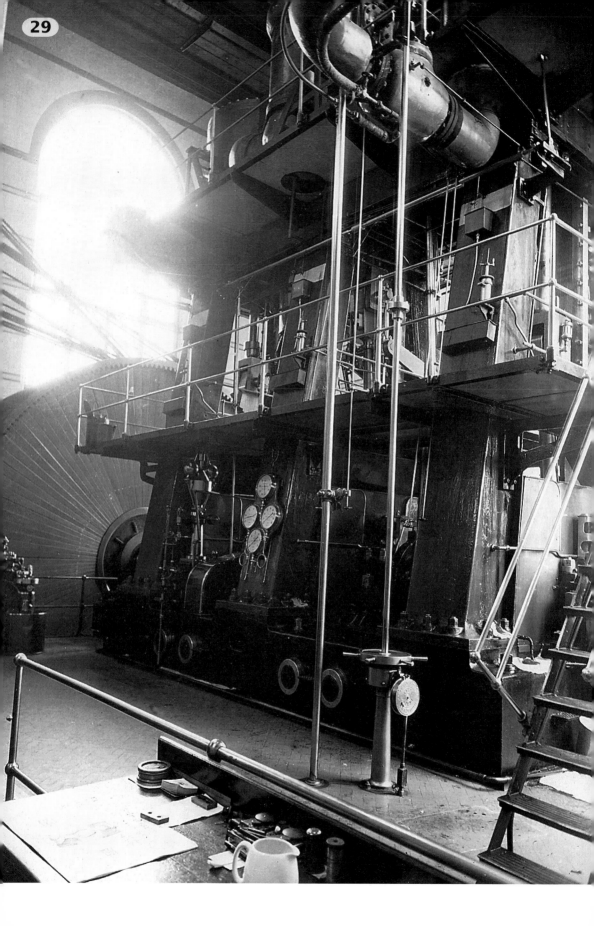

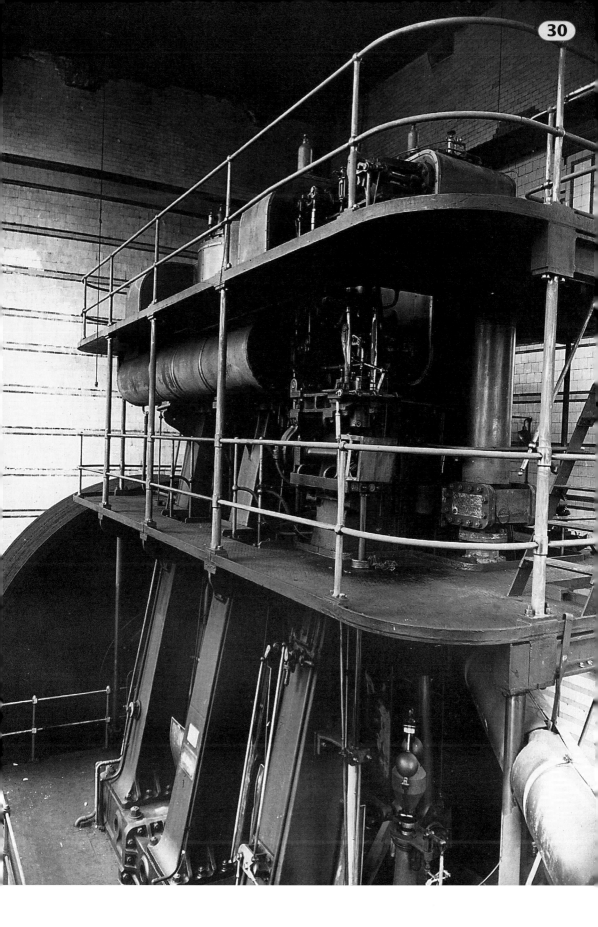

Three examples to illustrate small variations in this nearly standard type.

31 The Fir Mill, Royton, Lancs.

Cotton Spinning

Made by Scott & Hodgson in 1906, the 'Fir' engine developed 1,700hp at 81rpm. The Corliss-valve high-pressure cylinder was 21in bore, with the valves in line with the crankshaft, the intermediate-was 38in bore, with a single piston valve, and the 59in bore-low pressure was fitted with twin piston valves. With the higher speed, the flywheel was smaller, ie 22ft diameter, and 36 tons weight driving by 36 ropes. Steam was supplied at 160psi, without reduction for fifty years, by four Yates & Thom boilers until the mill closed. The raised part of the upper platform, to clear the exhaust pipe flange, and the twin piston valves for the low-pressure cylinder were Scott & Hodgson features.

32 The Hyde Spinning Co, Hyde, Cheshire.

Cotton Spinning

Hyde, built in 1906, was fitted with the standard Geo Saxon's triple so widely used in Lancashire cotton mills. Designed to develop 2,000hp, from Corliss-valve cylinders of 25, 38, and 60in bore, by 4ft stroke, it ran at 75rpm, and drove from the 21ft 6in flywheel by 40 ropes. Steam was supplied by the original four boilers at 180psi for 50 years until the mill closed. Typical Saxon features were that the high-and low-pressure valves were in line with the engine crankshaft, and the intermediate ones across it, the bed was in three sections joined by flanges, the maker's nameplate was clipped over the handrails, and the bracket carrying the air-pump lever was separate and bolted on. In No 31 it was cast with the column, requiring a special pattern.

33 The Lancashire Cotton Corporation, Royd Mill, Hollinwood.

Cotton Spinning

Royd, built in 1907, was one of the smaller mills, the engine built by J. & E. Wood of Bolton developing 900hp. The cylinders, of 18.5, 28.5, and 43in bore by 3ft 6in stroke, were all fitted with Corliss-valves, which in contrast to the maker's usual practice (see No 19) were fitted at the opposite sides of the cylinders. It ran at 94rpm, driving by 20 ropes from a 14ft flywheel. The original three Tetlow boilers still supplied steam at 180psi, when by 1961 electric drives were installed, and the engine was scrapped. The frame was unusual since there were only two columns in front, with twin feet to the single casting bed, the intermediate-cylinder being supported by a massive cross casting.

31

Three more examples, all with Corliss-valves, to illustrate slight differences in design.

34 The Croal Spinning Co, Bolton.

Cotton Spinning

'Shelagh' was built by Yates & Thom in 1908, to develop 1,300hp at 82rpm. The cylinders were 21.5, 34, and 55in bore by 4ft stroke, and were supplied with superheated steam at 160psi by three Yates & Thom boilers which retained the original working pressure fifty years later. Originally the mill was driven from the 22ft 6in flywheel by 36 ropes, but by 1957 the load consisted of three alternators driving the mill by motors; however, some years later the current was taken from the Grid, and the engine was scrapped. Interesting features were: that there was no entablature connecting the tops of the columns, but the cylinders were made monobloc by flange connections; that, like No 30, the high-pressure cylinder drove by a half or overhung crank, but was fitted with a box type of big end, whilst, most rare for vertical mill engines, each piston was fitted with a 2.5in diameter tail rod projecting through the top covers, working in tubular cases.

35 The English Combined Mills Co, Alder Mill, Leigh.

Cotton Spinning

Notable for being made by a concern better known for high-speed engines, the Alder was one of the three mill engines made by Browett & Lindley, Patricroft. The three cylinders, each fitted with Corliss-valves in line with the crankshaft, and separate from each other, were 22.08, 34, and 56in bore, all by 4ft stroke, and developed 1,800hp at 82rpm. Driving from the 22ft 6in flywheel by 45 ropes, the plant ran unaltered until scrapped when superseded by electric drives in the early 1960s. The four Tinker Shenton's boilers retained the original 200psi working pressure until the end.

36 Ormerod, Hardcastle & Co, Flash St Mill, Bolton.

Cotton Spinning

One of the few Irish engines fitted in Lancashire spinning mills, this was built by Victor Coates & Co, Belfast, in 1900. Designed to develop 1,000hp at about 85rpm, it was never fully loaded as the projected mill extension was not completed. The cylinders were 18, 28, and 48in bore by 3ft 6in stroke, all coupled together, and with the Corliss-valves all across the crankshaft centre line. The flywheel, fitted with the 'H' section arms used by Irish and Scottish builders, was 22ft diameter, grooved for 39 ropes to drive the mill floors. Like No 33, this was fitted with only two front columns, but at Flash St the centre cylinder was supported by two massive forged steel columns. It was scrapped when the mill was converted to electric drive in the late 1950s.

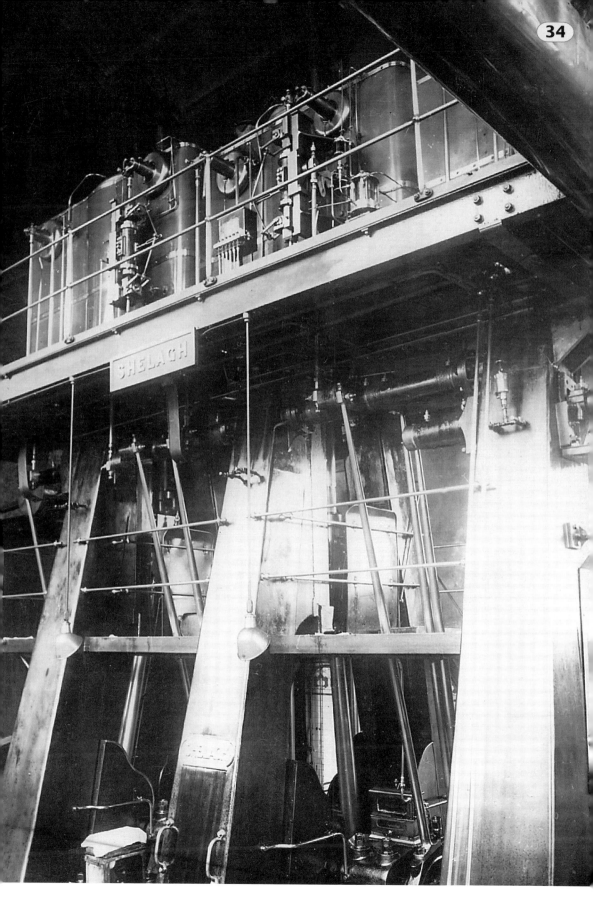

36

Three more triples, each made outside Lancashire and replacing an old beam engine, show other design features.

37 G. & R. Dewhurst Ltd, Arkwright Mill, Preston.

Cotton Spinning and Weaving

Until 1916 the mill and sheds were driven by gearing from a large double beam engine with six boilers working at 80psi, and my example was then fitted in an extensive re-organisation of power and drives. Made by Cole, Marchent & Morley of Bradford, it was fitted with their drop-piston valves, which, able to use high superheat, were highly economical and very quiet. Developing 1,500hp at $98^1/_2$ rpm, the cylinders were $23^3/_4$, 35, and 56in bore by 3ft stroke, with the valves driven from a single high-level camshaft. It drove the mill by ropes and the weaving shed by a heavy shaft and gearing, steam being supplied by four Tinker Shenton boilers at 160psi, superheated to 500°F, which in forty-three years' service needed only one rivet to be replaced. The original Preston square chimney, 200ft high by 18ft square at the base, still served the boilers. The single forged steel column in front of each cylinder, and the owner's monogram 'G.R.D.' worked in the tiles of the engine room were interesting features. Electric drives were installed in the 1960s.

38 Firth Bros, Shepley, Yorks.

Woollen Spinning

Another Yorkshire-made engine with steel columns in front, this had a very different history. It was made for Rank's flour mill, Hull, in the early 1900s, and after years of service was replaced by a larger Wood's engine when the mill was extended. The makers then removed it to Wm Whiteley's mill at Sowerby Bridge, where it gave good service until the mill was closed in 1937. It was then bought by Messrs Firth to replace their beam engine, and at the same time the gear drives were replaced by motors driven from the Wood's engine by the 400kW alternator seen on the right. This served for over twenty-five years until current was taken from the Grid. The Corliss-valve cylinders were 15, 22, and 34in bore by 3ft 6in stroke, using steam at 150psi, and driving by 16 ropes from the 16ft flywheel.

39 Langworthy Bros, Greengate Mills, Salford, Lancs.

Finished Cotton Goods

Langworthys made completely finished material from raw cotton, having at one time several engines and boiler plants in the large group of buildings. The spinning-mill engine was wrecked in a fire, and a Willan's engine was purchased new in 1904 to get things going quickly. Although the type was specifically designed for generating, several were used for rope-driving cotton mills. This one was No 3659, size T3, developing 850hp at 270rpm, with a complete triple-expansion engine on each crank, with low-pressure cylinders 32.3in bore by 13.9in stroke. The mill drives were retained intact, the new engine driving to the old mainshaft by 20 ropes from a 5ft pulley, to one of 12ft on the mill mainshaft. Costing £3,187, it gave yeoman service mostly under an engineer of the highest class, until the mills were closed in the late 1950s and all scrapped.

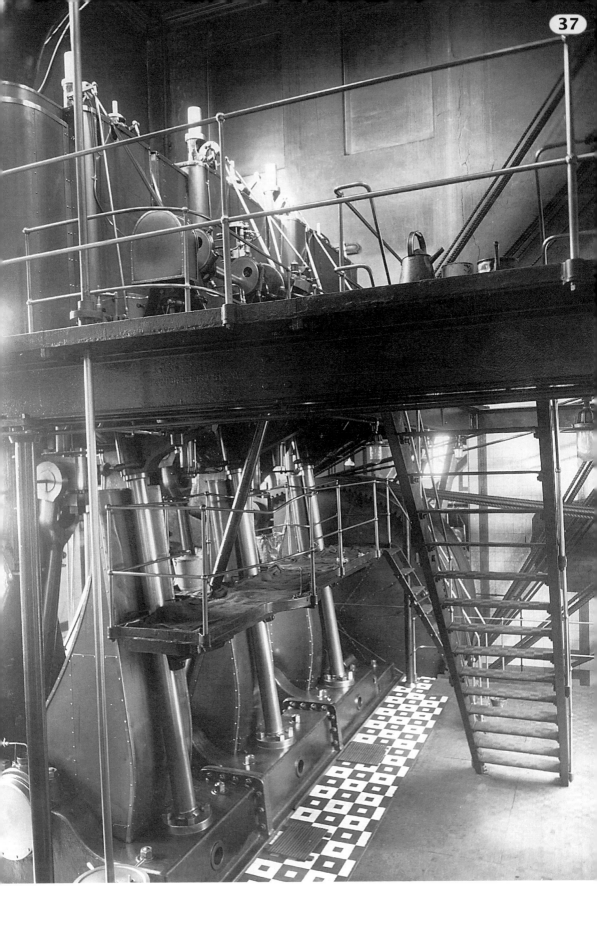

Less costly to construct, the compound engine gave very good economy, and, taking less space than the triple-expansion was much used by the smaller mills. My examples include one made in the heart of the weaving country, where most engines were horizontal.

40 Hutchinson & Pollock Ltd, Lodge Lane Rope Works, Liverpool.

Cordage Makers

Specialising on the Wheelock engine, Daniel Adamson also built slide-valve engines, and, latterly a small number with highly efficient drop-piston valves. This one was probably the last complete engine they built. It was made in 1912, to drive the existing plant and the extensions then completed, and developed 600hp from cylinders of 20 and 40in bore by 3ft 6in stroke, running at 80rpm with steam at 150psi. In contrast to No 37, the valves were driven by eccentrics on the crankshaft. Driving the plant by 16 ropes from the 14ft flywheel, it was an attractive engine which gave little trouble, whilst the 'Y' based columns and balanced cranks made for steady running. It was scrapped when the whole was converted to electric driving in 1956.

41 Stott & Smiths, Empire Mills, Congleton, Cheshire.

Towel Manufacturers

Like Petries, Burnley Ironworks built only three vertical engines. This one was built in 1900, again to drive an existing plant and extensions, totalling some 750 looms. The Corliss-valve high-pressure cylinder was 16in, and the low-pressure 30in bore by 2ft 6in stroke, the low-pressure having the semi-rotary slide-valves the makers often used, and it developed 250hp at 92rpm using steam at 120psi. Due to the location of the sheds the eight rope drives from the 10ft 6in flywheel were taken in opposite directions, and it ran as well as ever when fifty-five years old. The cross stays between the tops of the columns made a very rigid structure.

42 John Stott & Sons, Der St Mill, Todmorden.

Cotton Weaving

Vertical single-crank tandem engines were rare in the cotton trade, and this one, made by Wood Bros, Sowerby Bridge, for a mill in the nearby Craggs Valley, was removed, when that mill closed in the 1920s, to Der St to replace the engine installed there when it started in 1862. It developed 250hp as well as a 30hp lighting load in winter, having a Corliss-valve high-pressure cylinder 11in bore above the 22in slide-valve low-pressure which was on top of the columns. Named 'John Thomas', it gave very good service to both owners, driving by six ropes, but was scrapped when Der St closed in the 1950s.

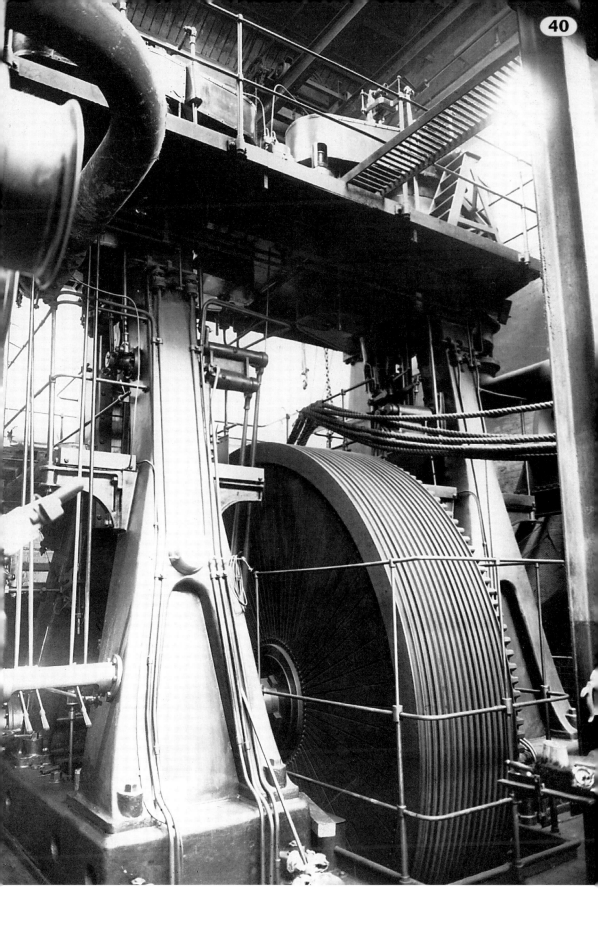

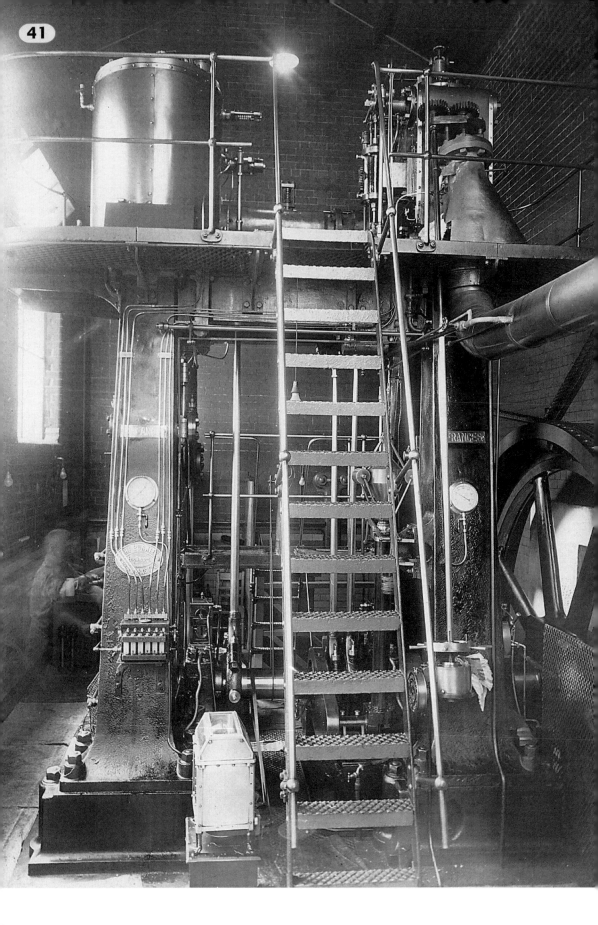

40

My last three examples of this type illustrate design variations from No 40 to 42, including a non-textile example.

43 J. W. Wheelwright (Cotton) Ltd, Rishworth, Yorks.

Cotton Spinning

Long celebrated for its wool and fabrics, Yorkshire also had a small cotton industry. Wheelwrights were situated upon a long-established corn mill site, and the mill, built in 1863, was originally driven by a splendid water wheel 57ft 6in diameter by 12ft 6in wide, built by Taylors of Marsden. This developed up to 240hp from the fall of about 60ft, but was always assisted by a double beam engine, the two being intercoupled to drive the several mill floors by gearing. The power and drives were re-organised about 1900, when the beam engine and gearing were removed, and replaced by a vertical compound engine and rope drives, again coupled to the waterwheel. The engine 'Emily' was built by Pollitt & Wigzell, and running at 85rpm developed up to 500hp, from Corliss-valve cylinders 17 and 34in bore by 4ft stroke, using superheated steam at 160psi. Interesting features were that the gearbox and base for the governor drive were cast in one with the engine bedplate, and the Pollitt style of rounded crank web. When, due to the owner's ill health, the mills were closed in 1948 the whole was sold and the engine scrapped, but the premises are still in use.

44 Buchanan's Flour Mills, Birkenhead Docks.

Flour and Provender Mills

Similar in size, this differed greatly from No 43. Built by Fairbairn, Lawson, Combe & Barbour of Belfast, it was believed to have been bought from an exhibition in 1907. The semi-enclosed or bottle type of framing was reminiscent of power-station design, and it probably drove a generator, the very light two-piece flywheel being fitted for the mill drive. Again fitted with Corliss-valves, the cylinders were about 18 and 30in bore by 3ft stroke. Driving the provender mill, this, like No 42, was little used when trade declined and later when the mills were converted to electric drive this, together with the J. & E. Woods' triple expansion engine working the flour mill, was scrapped.

45 John Harwood & Co, Woodside Mill No 2, Bolton.

Cotton Spinning

Another instance of power-station design adopted for mill drive, this type was specially developed by Hick Hargreaves of Bolton to work at higher speeds for the direct driving of generators. It was works No E 407. Fitted with Hicks high-speed crab-claw trip gear which worked very satisfactorily at speeds up to 127rpm, it readily produced the necessary 700hp, although it was a small engine, with cylinders about 17 and 32in bore by 2ft 6in stroke. Fully enclosed and with forced lubrication, it was an excellent engine which drove the mill through two rope pulleys until the mills were closed in 1958. The compactness gained by the higher speed is indicated by the fact that this 700hp engine was 5ft less in height than No 44, which developed some 250hp less.

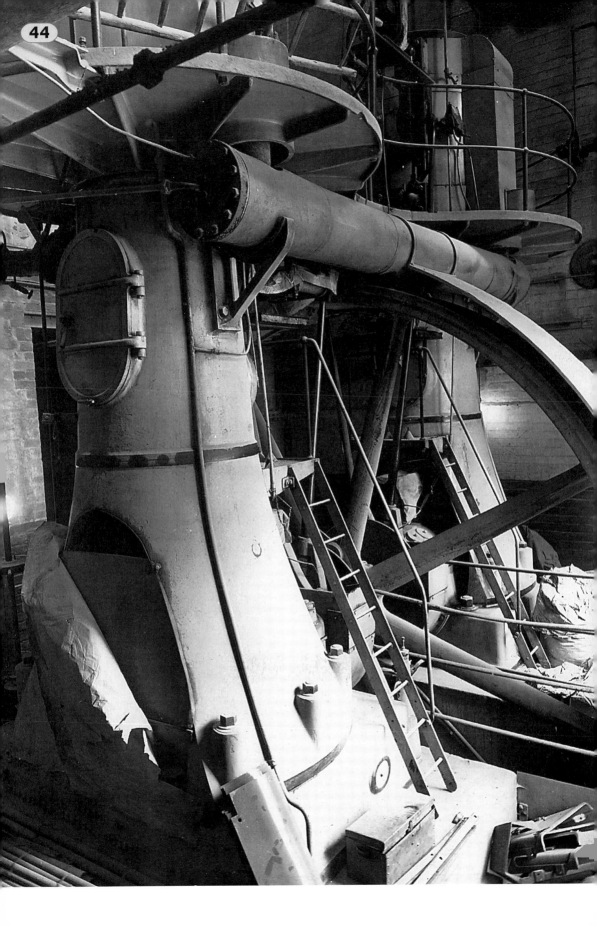

45

Uniflow engines, ie those in which the steam moved only in one direction, exhausting through ports at the end of the stroke, were known and built from 1827. They achieved little success until the type, specifically designed for high efficiency was re-introduced by Dr Stumpf of Berlin in 1908. Even then it was not easy to secure acceptance, in fact mechanical difficulties continued to arise even after taper boring was introduced to compensate for the effect of unequal heating on the cylinder bore.

46 Whittle & Turner Ltd, Progress Mill, Kirkham, Lancs.

Fabric Weaving

Following upon the reports of high economy in Europe, Musgraves of Bolton took out a licence to build uniflows in 1909, and from the first made for a Bolton mill in 1909, were soon building many. No 46 was installed in 1914, and drove the mill ever since. Developing 400hp, it ran unaltered except that, to reduce cylinder wear, a tail rod and slide, together with a lightweight piston were fitted by Galloways in 1929. The cylinder was $26^1/_2$in bore by 2ft stroke, and it ran at 130rpm using steam at 160psi. The short stroke, high revolutions, total enclosure, and forced lubrication were all characteristic uniflow features. At one time driving 1,000 looms and latterly after re-spacing 800, it must have been the best investment in the trade, tribute alike to the builders, and the fine engineers and sound management who equally contributed to this result. The original Musgrave boiler together with one by Thompsons fitted later, still served in 1966, and the reciprocating camshaft was not changed.

47 The Croston Manufacturing Co, Croston, Nr Preston.

Cotton Weaving

Other concerns soon began to build uniflows, and at least two firms in Bolton, two in Blackburn, one in Manchester, and others in Yorkshire did so. The Croston Co was established in 1887, having a cross compound engine gear-driving the original shed. More capacity was required in 1922, a new shed was built, and 'Edward Walmsley', made by Yates & Thom of Blackburn in 1924 was installed to drive the new and the old sections. A new boiler by Fosters for 160psi was installed and ran the old engine at reduced pressure until the new engine was ready. The latter developed 450hp, from a cylinder $27^1/_2$in bore by 2ft 6in stroke, running at 140rpm and using superheated steam at the full boiler pressure. It will be noted that Nos 46 and 47 are examples where the higher engine speed allowed the engine to be coupled directly to the mainshaft, also that No 47 has a rotating sideshaft drive for the valves.

48 Barlow & Jones, Prospect Mill, Bolton.

Cotton Spinning and Weaving

Made in 1925, this was the largest and almost the last uniflow made by Musgraves. Designed to develop 1,600hp at 120rpm, the cylinder was 40in bore by 3ft 8in stroke, driving by 40 ropes to the mill and a 525kW alternator for the weaving shed. No air pump was fitted for the condenser, the vacuum being maintained by a Musgrave Radojet air ejector. As with No 46 this engine in later years was fitted with a lightweight piston and tail rod, all being scrapped when electric driving was installed.

Three examples made outside Lancashire indicate that design varied very little wherever they were made.

49 Messrs Dobroyd Ltd, New Mills, Nr Holmfirth.

Fine Woollen Fabrics

Pollitt & Wigzell made their first uniflow engine in 1924, and, jealous of their reputation, tried it out in their own works first. It was wasted concern, however, since this very good engine, after providing power for the works until they closed in 1929, was installed at the Dobroyd Mills in 1932, where it still gave fine service thirty-five years later, driving an alternator by ropes. 'Anne' as she was later called, always ran at a leisurely 80rpm, to develop 500hp with high economy, and in contrast to many uniflows was built with a tail rod.

50 Laidlaws, Allers Mill, Jedburgh.

Blanket Weaving

My Scottish example was constructed by Douglas & Grant of Kirkcaldy (their works No 704) and built in 1919. Replacing the two previous engines with great economy, 'Jedwater' ran at 130rpm, developing 200hp. This was coupled directly to the mill mainshaft which ran down one side of the weaving shed, and drove the other side by belts. The only gearing was that which coupled the waterwheel to the mill, but after working together for forty years the gearing of the waterwheel was destroyed by grit in a flood, and the uniflow then drove the whole until the mill was closed about five years later. Typical of the makers' work, it gave no trouble, but, in contrast to most enclosed engines, this was drip oiled from external lubricators fed by recirculated oil. Another distinctive feature was that the condenser was on the engine room floor, with the air pump driven from the piston tail rod.

51 Eckersleys, Wigan, No 3 Western Mill.

Cotton Spinning

The main engine for the Western mill was a J. & E. Wood's McBeth's patent triple-expansion vertical engine installed in 1900, which developed 1,100hp, but when this was overloaded by new machinery in 1922, No 51 was installed to assist it. Made by Robeys of Lincoln, it was one of the few engines from that county to work in Lancashire, and developed 300hp at 160rpm from a cylinder 22in bore by 2ft stroke. It was regularly used until, in the 1960s, the business was re-organised, several of the mills dismantled, and the remainder converted to electric drive. There were five engines and sixteen boilers in all in the 1940s.

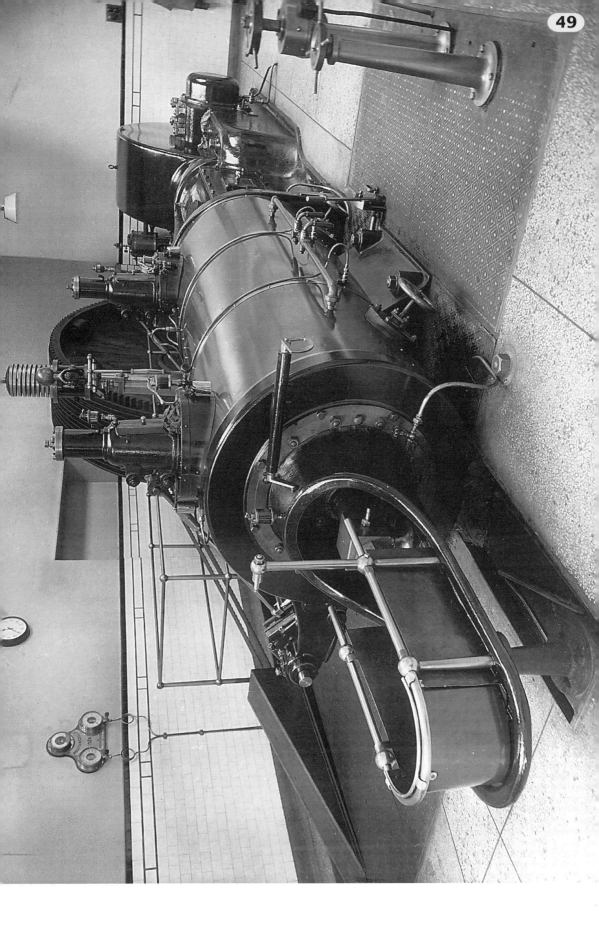

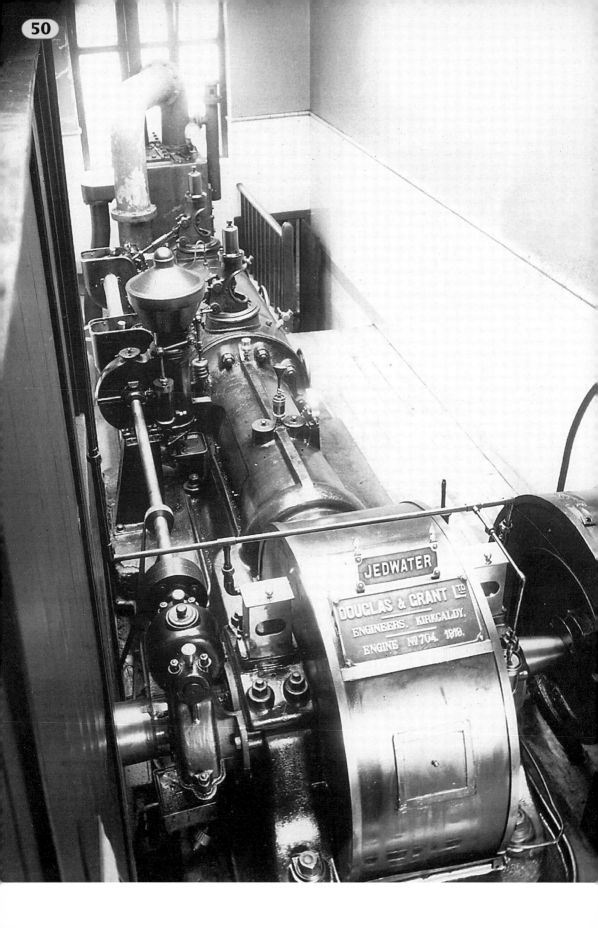

Twin mills often resulted from using the profit from the first to build the second, and when mills were planned for this, either the first engine was made large enough to drive both, as at Mons (No 26), or Moston (Part 1 No 54), a procedure which gave us some splendid engines, or the first engine room was designed for extension, as Nos 52-53 below.

52 Swan Lane Mill Co, Bolton, Nos 1 and 2 mills.

Cotton Spinning

A fine example of management at its best, Swan Lane not only completed the original twin mill plan, but in 1914 built the No 3 mill. No 1 was built in 1903, and driven by the left-hand engine, a cross compound by Geo Saxon of Manchester, works No 352. Developing 1,300hp at 62rpm, the cylinders were 26 and 52in bore by 5ft stroke, which, using steam at 160psi, drove the mill by 35 ropes from the 26ft flywheel. The fine arches and columns were provided at the start, and were filled with brickwork until No 2 mill was completed in 1906, when the engine room was extended, and No 2 engine, identical with No 1, but running at 65rpm to develop 1,400hp, was installed. The two thus drove the No I mill to the left, and No 2 to the right, retaining the brick wall between the two rope races to reduce the fire risk. Ten boilers in one row continued to steam the mill and the three engines until, in 1959, motor-driven ring frames were installed, but one of the engines continued to drive the lower floor of No 1 and No 2 mills for some time after.

53 Broadstone Mills, Reddish, Stockport.

Cotton Spinning

Broadstone, like Swan Lane, was planned for an extension which was completed, but the plan was quite different, since although the rope race was central, and divided by a brick wall, the power plants were entirely separate, as Nos 1 and 2 mill each had its own boiler house with four boilers and separate chimney. Built in 1906 and 1907, with the mills, the engines, identical but of opposite hand, were made by Geo Saxons with Corliss-valve cylinders 22, 35, and 54in bore by 4ft stroke, developing 1,500hp at 75rpm when supplied with steam at 200psi. Typical Saxons' plain design, with the intermediate-pressure valves across the engine centre line, they gave exemplary service until the mills were closed in 1959, when with other usage the whole plant was scrapped.

54 Dobroyd Ltd, New Mills, Nr Holmfirth, Yorks.

Fine Woollen Cloth

Another delightful plant with twin engines, this time of Yorkshire manufacture, the Dobroyd engines always drove electrically by rope-driven alternators. No 1 engine, that across the top, is my No 49, 'Anne', which was joined in 1955 by 'Jane' seen on the right, whose history differed greatly. Made by Woodhouse & Mitchell in 1920 for Dover Mills, she worked there until they were closed, and was then moved to Taylor Liveseys at Slathwaite. After considerable service there she was removed when, owing to increased power needs, they turned over to electric driving, and then gave good service at Denehouse Mill at Holmfirth until this closed, when in 1955 she came to Dobroyd. Designed to run at 132rpm, 'Jane' unlike 'Anne' never had a tail rod.

52

Two more examples of the twin-engine theme, concluding with one with four engines in a single room.

55 Thos Henry Shaw Ltd, Wapping Mills, Bradford.

Woolcombing

Another instance of two Yorkshire engines in one room, these are described in Part 1, Nos 55 and 56, and differ from No 54, Part 2, in that, again by different makers, they were supplied at the same time and always worked in the same engine room. Driving to the typical woolcombers' single main shafts, they represented the best in Yorkshire engineering and giving exemplary service, frequently ran day and night, from their installation in 1911 to the change-over to electric driving in 1965, a credit alike to the makers, owners, and engineers.

56 Learoyd Bros & Co, Mirfield.

Worsted Manufacturers

Another pair of Yorkshire tandems, made by Pollit & Wigzell, but of their three-piston-rod design (see *Stationary Steam Engine*, Engine No 19). The left-hand engine was one of two identical ones installed in 1898, each developing 170hp from a Corliss high-pressure of $11^{1}/_{2}$in and a slide-valve low-pressure 23in bore by 3ft6in stroke, running at 80rpm on steam of 120psi. They drove to one mainshaft for the weaving shed and lighting generators. More power was needed in 1905, and the right-hand engine was replaced by 'Elizabeth' of the same design but 300hp. They gave typical Pollitt's service until, with new looms and electric drives installed, the engines were scrapped in the late 1950s.

57 John Dugdale & Bros Ltd, Lowerhouse Mills, Burnley, Lancs.

Cotton Spinning and Weaving

Beginning in 1796, the business grew, and No 1 engine, a double beam by Hick of Bolton with cylinders 37in bore by 7ft stroke was installed in 1838. It was followed in 1844 by No 2, a double beam by Marslands of Burnley with cylinders 34in by 6ft stroke, the two developing some 650hp with steam at 35psi. By 1865, the boilers were worn, and more power was needed, so new boilers for 65psi were installed. The Marsland engine was then pusher compounded by the installation of a twin horizontal engine 20in bore by 3ft stroke made by Clayton & Goodfellows (works Nos 78 and 79) gearing to the same mainshaft, and followed by Clayton & Goodfellows Nos 116 and 117, 23in by 3ft 6in, for the Hick beam in 1867. The whole thus developed over 1,200hp, but by 1930 when the mills closed, power was supplied by two McNaught compounded beam engines, one with a 48in belt drive; no record of this remains, however.

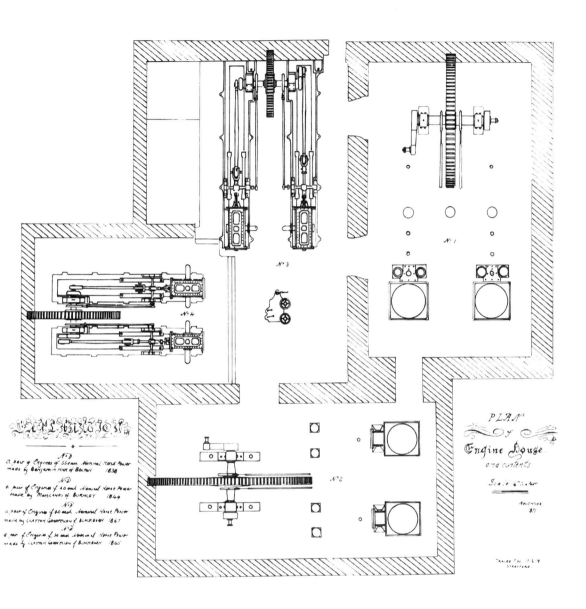

N.º 3

N.º 4

N.º 1

N.º 2

PLAN
of
Engine House
and contents

Scale ⅛ Inch

November
1871

Traced C.W. 17.5.74
Stretford

The predominance of Lancashire in the cotton story tends to overshadow the part played by the neighbouring county of Cheshire. An extensive spinning and weaving trade, together with large bleaching and finishing industries, developed there, but more to our interest are the fine engines which, together with a large output of boilers, were made there.

58 Astley Mill, Dukinfield.

Cotton Spinning

Surely, in 'Constance', Astley had one of the most delightful mill engines. Built in 1885 by Goodfellows & Matthews, Hyde, she was designed to develop 1,300hp at 50rpm, using steam at 100psi. The cylinders were 32 and 60in bore by 7ft stroke, with the valves below, operated by Ramsbottom's trip gear, driving by a 32ft flywheel 6ft wide, grooved for 34 ropes. This flywheel weighed 80 tons. The crankshaft bearings were 17in diameter by 3ft 4in total length. She ran the successful mill, frequently overloaded, until despite every effort, the depression of the 1930s compelled closure. The open-work cast-iron floor plates, massive trunk frames, very neat lagging, and the marine-type starting platform were all the maker's design features at the period. The total weight was 215 tons, and the low-pressure exhaust valves, 19in diameter, were probably as large as any fitted to a mill engine.

59 Newton Moor Spinning Co, Victoria Mill, Newton Moor, Nr Hyde.

Cotton Spinning

Daniel Adamson of Dukinfield early foresaw that multi-stage expansion must come to the fore in mill engines, and his patent No 52 of 1861 covered triple-expansion engines and interstage reheat. When he was asked to provide the engine for this mill in 1863, he put the ideas into practice with a twin triple-expansion engine with cylinders 11, 22, and 38in bore by 6ft stroke, which used parallel motion to guide the crossheads. When the adjacent Albert Mill was built in 1874, he provided a four-cylinder quadruple-expansion engine with rocking valves. Both were successful and economical, but cotton spinning ceased many years ago.

60 Minerva Mill, Dukinfield.

Cotton Spinning

When, in 1892, he engined the Minerva, 'Owd Dan', as he was affectionately called, provided a very different design to No 59. Again triple-expansion, it was of the Wheelock type, which Adamsons built under licence after its success at the Paris Exhibition of 1878. The cylinders were 22, 36, 40, and 40in bore by 6ft stroke, and it developed 1,500hp at 55rpm using steam at 160psi. The later Wheelock valves comprised flat grids which, sliding over the faces by a toggle action, gave very rapid opening and closing. The valves and port faces were machined upon plugs which, separate from the cylinders and fitting with a slight taper, could be withdrawn and replaced by a spare unit. Like Astley, Minerva was a victim of the depression, and after closing, the mill was pulled down, leaving one to wonder that so much was produced from so little space.

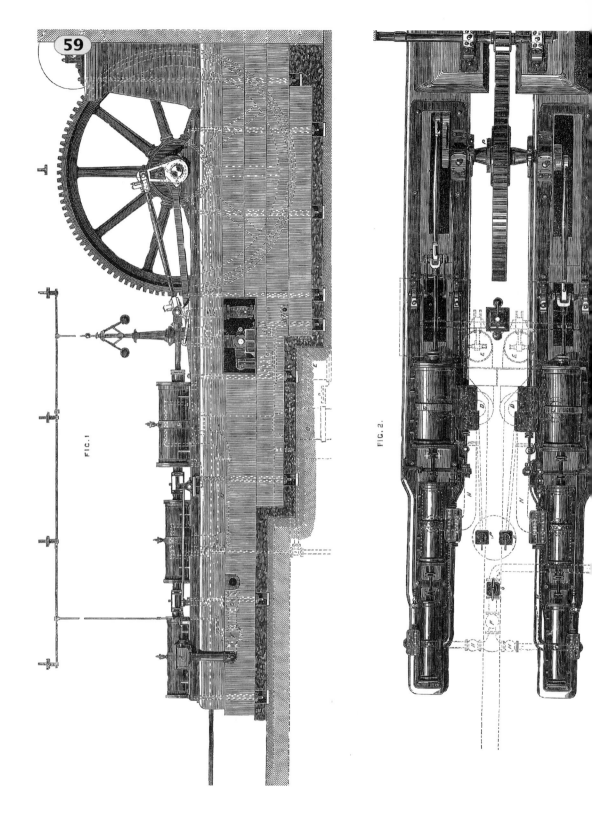

FIG. 1

FIG. 2.

60

Engineering in England owes much to the Scots mechanics who in the late eighteenth century came to England to play a large part in the development of the textile trade. That this trend did not drain all of the talent, however, is shown by the engineering industry of the Clyde and, as these examples show, magnificent mill engines were constructed in Scotland as long as they continued to be built.

61 Douglas & Grant, Kirkcaldy

Douglas & Grant, Kirkcaldy adopted Corliss-valves as soon as they were introduced and together with much machinery for the rice trade built large mill engines for the growing textile trade of the Far East. No 61 is typical of these, and was built for the Marayon Spinning & Manufacturing Company in 1888. Developing 2,500hp at 60rpm, the cylinders were 40 and 70in bore by 6ft stroke, and used steam at 100psi. The drive was from the 30ft flywheel which, weighing 100 tons, was 8ft 6in wide and grooved for 38 ropes. It was typical of Scottish practice where nothing was spared to make a sound job.

62 James Carmichael, Dundee

James Carmichael were engineers in the widest sense who beside much machinery for the jute trade, made delightful engines for mills.

(A) Again developing 2,500hp this, made in the early 1900s, used steam at a higher pressure and was of slightly smaller dimensions. The single mainshaft drive suggests that it may have been for a jute mill. The magnificent finish is a credit to all concerned.

(B) This 2,000hp triple-expansion example again shows the very stiff design, also the unusual feature of placing the valve gear operating shaft at mid engine height.

63 Fullerton, Hodgart & Barclay, Paisley

Fullerton, Hodgart & Barclay were also engineers of wide scope who made fine mill engines. It was therefore natural that when Paisley concerns, in their numerous expansions, added to their mills, some at least of the engines were locally made.

(A) An example of the designs that followed the beam-engine period, this developed about 2,000hp from cylinders approximately 27 and 50in bore by 5ft stroke. By any standard, the finish is superb throughout, and with the quietude of the slide-valves, must have been delightful. It was of the twin tandem type.

(B) Was built in 1888 to develop 2,000hp at 50rpm. The cylinders were 33 and 63in bore by 7ft stroke, and it drove through a flywheel 32ft in diameter by 34 ropes. Together with the Musgrave engine beside it, which had cylinders of the same dimensions, the whole was a delightful example of the owners' and builders' pride in the plant, but with the march of progress electrical driving and new machinery superseded the engines by a steam turbine generating station, highly economical yet surely leaving us the poorer for the loss of such delightful plant.

61

The engines considered so far were the standard types, but to meet the needs for more power and economy where space was restricted special designs were evolved, as the following illustrate.

64 Halsteads, Stanley Mill, Bradford, Yorks.

Woollen Weaving

This was made in 1883, by Cole, Booth & Porter, who appear to have built three engines only. It was a triple-expansion engine with the three cylinders of 10, 16, and 24in bore by 4ft stroke set in a triangle driving to a single crosshead and crank. All were fitted with slide-valves, with a governor-controlled cut-off valve for the high pressure. It developed 350hp at 80rpm on steam at 120psi, driving the several loom shafts by 12 ropes from the 16ft 6in flywheel. Stanley was an efficient mill which had electric lighting early in the 1890s. The driving ropes gave good service, and two of those seen had run for 55 and others for over 30 years. The compactness of the engine is indicated by the 20ft length of its bed, but it was scrapped when electric driving was installed in 1956, the plant closing a few years later.

65 The Hall Lane Spinning Company, Leigh.

Cotton Spinning (1914)

The vertical-horizontal design, although built many years before, really came into its own with the wonderful Manhattan generating plant in New York in 1904, and Hall Lane was one of several which George Saxon built to this design in the early 1900s. Developing 1,400hp at 75rpm, the horizontal drop-valve high-pressure cylinder was 27in bore and the Corliss-valve low-pressure was 54in bore by 4ft 6in stroke. Both cylinders drove on to one single-web counterbalanced crank, the power being distributed to the mill from the 22ft 6in flywheel, originally by 40 ropes, but after an accident the upper floors, and eventually the whole mill, was converted to motor drives, the mill closing a few years later. The engine and engine-room were Lancashire practice at its best, and no mill engine had a finer entry to the rope race that than seen at the left.

66 The Elk Mill Company, Royton, Lancs.

Cotton Spinning

The turbine was the most compact of all mill drives, frequently adopted to replace old power units, though some mills were specially built for turbine drive. Elk, of 1926, the last steam-driven cotton spinning mill built in the UK, was thus. The double-cylinder Parsons turbine, works No 2028, developed 2,600hp at 5,000rpm and drove through a gearbox which, reducing the speed to 333rpm, drove the Elk mill by 50 ropes from the 5ft pulley on the right, and the Shiloh mill nearby from the 728kW alternator on the left. Superheated steam at 260psi was supplied from four Daniel Adamson boilers in a highly economical plant, and the turbines and gearbox were only 16ft long overall.

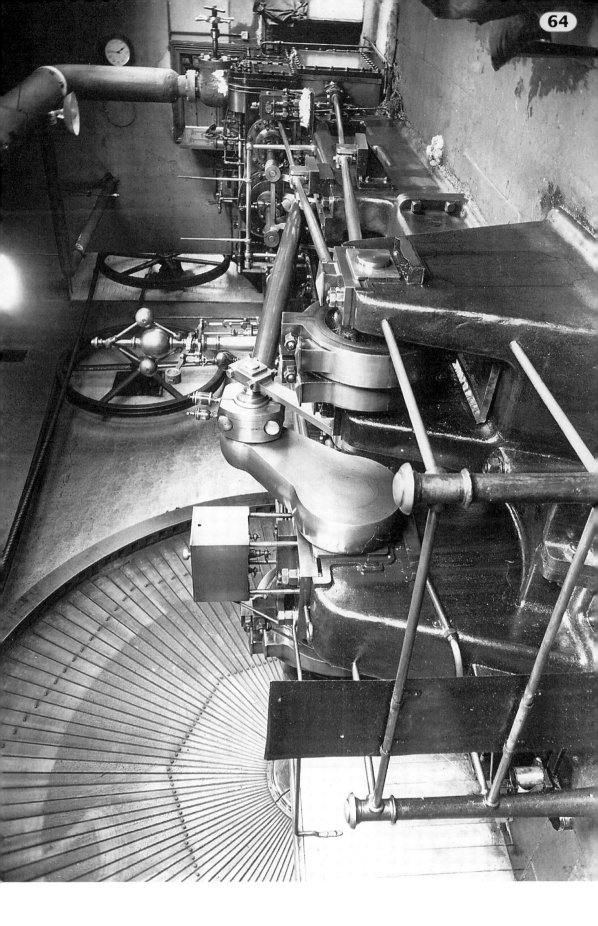

66

The boiler story was much less involved than that of the engines, since once rising pressure made circular boilers essential, the Lancashire type with two flues soon became standard. Used in Cornwall many years before, it was patented by Fairbairn & Hetherington in 1844, and its steady steaming, and the strength of the small flues (the large single flue of the Cornish boiler was weak), soon led to its wide use. Within the broad framework of twin flues in a large shell, many improvements were made, so that in later years, with good engineers, mill boilers (Swan Lane, Bolton, had ten in a row) were often insured for the original pressure 60 years later, and the Nile set, built for 160psi in 1899, was insured for 170psi sixty years later. The largest ever built were 12ft diameter for Salts (30psi-1872), and the highest pressure was Elk Mill (260psi-1926). Production soon became big business, leading to the establishment of many small firms, whilst the sheer growth of production led firms like Galloways (who for many years made a boiler per day), Hicks, and Musgraves to build separate boiler works. Despite the largely standard design, the cost varied widely, and when six boilers were required in London in 1890, 24 tenders were received varying from £416 (Andertons, Accrington) to £722 (Harveys, Hayle) per boiler, the contract going to Spurr, Inman, Wakefield (£470 each). Production was well organised, and at Galloways, Ardwick, the construction of the shell and flues went on in parallel shops, meeting at the top where, the endplate waiting, the whole was soon assembled. Greens of Wakefield, too, made economisers on a highly developed flow-line of moulding, casting, machining, and testing, which with efficient erecting staff, provided the millions of feed-water heating pipes which undoubtedly saved more fuel for industry than any other single invention.

67 Queen Mill, Dukinfield

67 of **Queen Mill, Dukinfield,** shows what a good firebeater (there were no 'stokers' in textile mills), with a good engineer and management made of a firehole, where a skilled man would make 7,500lb of steam per boiler per hour, and with good fuel not vary the steam pressure 2psi all day.

68 A & B

68 A & B **from Musgrave's catalogue,** illustrates the construction of a Lancashire boiler, how it was set in brickwork, and the fittings needed for safe working. It also shows the economisers invented by E. Green in 1845, which consisted of banks of cast-iron pipes, usually 4in diameter by 9ft long. Fitted in the flues between the boiler and the chimney they raised the feed-water temperature nearly 200°F. An economiser can be seen on the extreme right of plate 68b.

67

68a

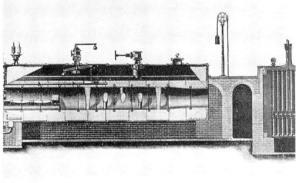

68b

Three variations from the basic Lancashire form arose in later years, each of them designed to give more steam in a smaller space. These were Galloway, three-flue, and Yorkshire.

69

(a) shows a set of **Galloway** boilers ready to be bricked in, and indicates that they were no different at the front end. The plain circular flues were, however, only about one-third of the length of the shell, and were then combined into a single flue containing numerous Galloway taper water tubes. At first oval in section, the flue was later made kidney shaped to resist higher pressure.

(b) shows the rear end of a Galloway boiler, the flues around it, and the kidney-shaped flue and water tubes.

(c) **The three-flue**, in which a smaller flue was placed in the dead space below the twin flues of the Lancashire type. Certainly made in Burnley in the 1860s, it was made by other firms in later years, but was never popular, as the extra flue made cleaning difficult.

(d) **The Yorkshire**, the latest of all, was patented by W. H. Casmey in 1906. It reverted to the twin plain flues of the Lancashire, but they were made tapering, being small in diameter at the front where the furnaces were, to the largest that the shell would contain at the rear, whilst they were also made to rise toward the rear. Shorter than the Lancashire, it was free steaming, and gave great satisfaction to users. A considerable number was made over some 20 years.

69a

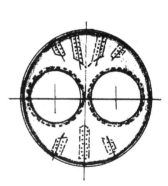

69c

69b

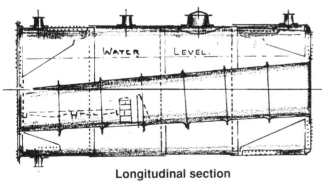

Longitudinal section

69d

Back end elevation

Front end elevation

The early mills of Lombe, Strutt, and Arkwright used traditional millwork, transmitting the power by wooden shafts and gearing. The first major improvement was the use of cast iron for this purpose in the late eighteenth century, but the wooden shafts and pulleys were still used in the rooms. The next development came in the 1820s, when Fairbairn replaced these by light wrought-iron shafts which, revolving at higher speeds with the smaller pulleys needed, greatly improved the lighting in the rooms. Nasmyth proposed the use of small engines in each section, but this was little used in the cotton mills. The greatest single advance came in the 1860s when belts and ropes were adopted for main drives from the engines, which set the pattern that served until electric power divorced the prime mover from the power user. Sometimes rope transmission to parts of the mill was used from geared engine drive, but it was not good practice unless the rope speeds were low, since the flexible ropes caused backlash in the gearing. Geared drive comprised either teeth fitted upon the flywheel arms (see Nos 4, 7, 8, 12, and 17, Part 1, and 3, 5, 9, and 21, Part 2), or upon the rim (see Nos 9, 10, 14, 16, 21, 22, 23, 30, 36, and 66, Part 1, and 4, 57, 59, and 70, Part 2), to a pinion on the second motion shaft, and thence by bevel wheels to the mill shafts. Very compact, the drive was carried through the floors without large apertures which could carry fire. The gears were aligned and held upon the shafts by thin taper wedges called stakes, which were fitted to flats on the shaft and wheel hub. Staking, as it was called, had to be done with great skill, since the stakes alone held the gears in alignment and resisted the driving stresses. A problem with vertical shafts was the need to support the weight, and one such shaft at Bradford, transmitting 1,000hp at 112rpm, weighed over 40 tons with the wheels. The heating of the lower or footstep bearing was difficult to cure, and one persistent Lancashire offender was finally cured by forcing oil at 1,000psi beneath the shaft end.

The comparison between geared and rope drives can be best illustrated by a mill at Ashton under Lyne. No 70 shows the mill as it was built in the 1850s, with a double beam engine driving by teeth on the flywheel rim to a pinion on the second motion shaft, and thence to the spinning mill floors on the left by bevel gears and vertical shaft. It will be noted that each set of wheels increased the speed, so reducing the size of the shafts. The second motion shaft was also carried to the right along the wall of the single floor weaving shed. The looms were driven by belts from shafts which, at right angles to the second motion, again were driven by bevel wheels, a layout which persisted as long as weaving sheds were driven mechanically. The drawings also illustrate the addition, some twenty years later, of a high-pressure pusher engine which, taking steam at about 80psi from new boilers, exhausted this to the beam engine. The use of separate gearing allowed the engines to be run at different speeds. The mill ran economically in this way for over 50 years.

Round cotton ropes driving by grooves in the flywheel and pulleys and each transmitting about 50hp at 5,000ft per minute rope speed, were unequalled as long as central prime movers drove cotton mills. The failure of one of several ropes driving a floor did not stop production and it was the cheapest to install; in one case belts were quoted at £324 and ropes for the same drive at £73. Rope driving flywheels were regularly built up to 30ft diameter, with at least two of

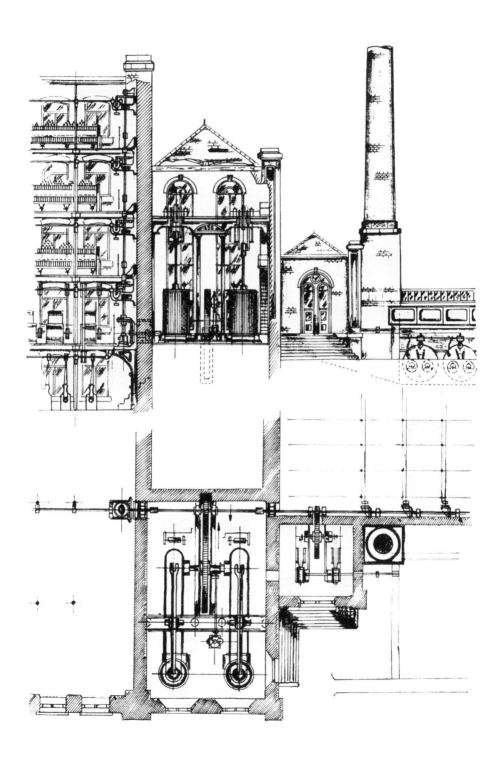

70

34ft in Lancashire and one of 36ft in Scotland. The widest wheel was that built for the Pear Mill, Bredbury, which, made in three sections totalling 13ft 8in wide, had 73 grooves for the ropes which the 3,500hp would have needed had the twin mill scheme been completed. Although used in the USA, continuous drives comprising a single rope passing around all of the pulleys, and tightened by a loaded tension pulley, were little used in the UK, although the system permitted the use of small pulleys, short centres, and odd angle drives. From their large size it might be assumed that cotton mills were not accurately laid out, but this was not so. When Swan Lane mill No 2 was built (see No 52, Part 2), four years after No 1, it was laid out so accurately that when, fifty years later, the mills were partly converted to electric drive, it was desired to drive the two bottom rooms from one engine, it was found that the mainshafts were so exactly set that it was possible to couple those of No 1 and No 2 mills together with very little adjustment.

Flat leather belts, running on smooth faced pulleys, were long used for main drives in the USA, and were adopted in Britain in the 1860s. No 49, Part 1, illustrates this, but the finest example was at Messrs Clark's Thread Mills at Paisley, where the Atlantic and Pacific Mills were each divided by a central belt well in which a Musgrave double beam engine, through twin countershafts, drove a total of sixteen belts to the room shafts for half a century. Steel belts were used in Alsace in the 1860s, and there was a return to these from 1912 to 1922 for main drives from engines, and although many were converted to rope drives later, No 39, Part 1, and No 22, Part 2, were successful examples which ran for many years. They ran on flat rims faced with cork coated with dressing. The difference between gear and rope drive is indicated by No 71, of the same mill as No 70.

When in later years the engines and gearing were badly worn, Messrs Saxons of Manchester were called in to produce a complete re-arrangement of the power plant and drives, but this fine scheme was not completed as the mill closed in the depression. It consisted of a cross compound Corliss-valve engine placed in the beam engine room, driving by ropes to a new second motion shaft, which due to the length of the rope drive was placed beyond the old engine room. It then drove back to the original room shafts in the mill and shed, as well as a dynamo for lighting. The new rope race and second motion shaft were to be housed in a glazed rope race, whilst the shed ropes were within the shed itself. In this case, the room was available for the alterations, but it serves to indicate the difficulties which faced the engineers when the mill had been built all around the original engine rooms. Despite this, however, they never failed to find a way out, as long as the mill was prepared to pay the very reasonable prices asked.

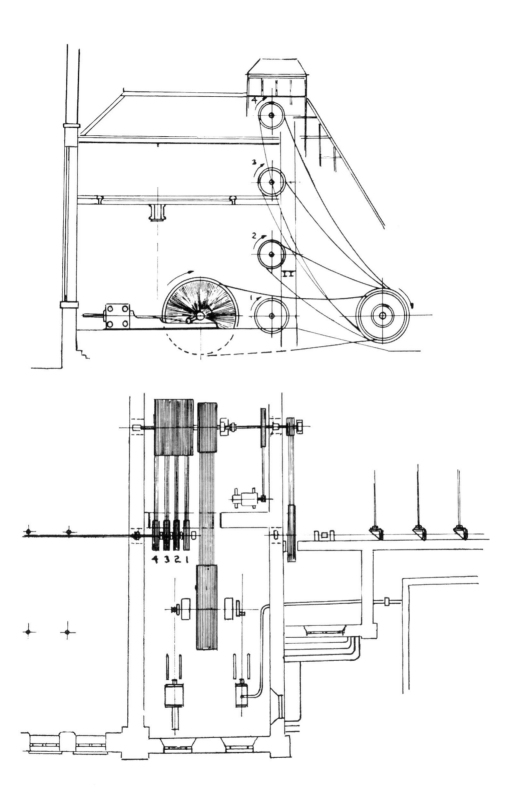

71

These were of two broad types, ie the spinning mill in which cotton was spun into yarn and the weaving shed in which yarn was woven into cloth.

The spinning mill was a multi-storied building, usually with five or six floors, but sometimes more, although at least two, Cromer at Middleton and Empress at Wigan, had a single floor only. Such mills were rectangular in plan, the proportions being determined by the size and layout of the machines; if the mules were longwise, the mill was long and narrow, but where they were across the rooms, the mill was wide and short. The risk of fires in the preparation section early led to that dangerous section being isolated from the rest of the mill by massive walls which, usually about a quarter of the length along, were used to carry the heavy vertical shafts which drove the mill by gearing. The engine in this case could be outside, driving to the vertical shaft through the bottom room within the mill, beside the upright shafts as at United, or as at Rock, where the drive was a shaft in a tower outside of the mill.

The introduction of wrapping drives, ie belts and ropes, about 1870, left little scope for such variations, since the engine and mill shafts had to be parallel, and at a suitable distance to give a good lead from the flywheel to the pulleys. This is seen at the Eclipse mill (No 72a), a layout which served until rope-driven mills ceased to be built, but such was the ingenuity of the mill architects, that almost every conceivable arrangement was adopted to suit local conditions, and with inverted vertical engines a twin mill could have them at the centre as at Broadstone, or at the end as at Marlborough. The later mills built of red stock brick were superb structures which needed little repair in 50 to 80 years, although due to rising costs the mills were less substantial after 1900.

The weaving shed was usually a single floor. No 72b shows Brownside shed, Burnley, which was built of stone in the 1850s, and driven by a beam engine placed in the house seen beside the chimney. It ran with little alteration for over sixty years, when the original engine was replaced by a Pollitt horizontal engine in a house built beside the original one. This engine ran until the mill closed some fifty years later. Sheds were usually sited in the valleys for humidity, and built to suit the rising ground of the valley sides. The roof was arranged with a steeply inclined glass front facing north if possible, which gave very even lighting all the year. Building on the valley sides led to various drive layouts so that the engine was sometimes above the shed and drove downwards, or vice versa, sometimes with a rope angle of nearly 45 degrees. The standard drive arrangement was a shaft along the side of the shed with shafts at right angles across the shed driven by bevel gears from the main shaft, the power allowed being one half horse power per loom.

72a

72b

Engine Building

And what of engine making? With increasing business, constructional departments were more organised, but since every engine comprised many separate highly finished small parts, the machining and erecting shops were always in seeming confusion. Yet the larger shops were designed to give an even flow of work, and this was an early feature of Hicks, Nasmyths, and other works. Smaller shops could not do this, and the apparent confusion there was often the result of a heavy demand for one type of machining which meant that parts needing this had to be allocated for maximum production. James Watt, starting from scratch in engine building and harassed by the demand for engines, early found that it was necessary to develop special skills in men, so that, with some good at nozzles, others with air pumps, boring, or making working gear he was able to supply more readily the specialised parts which alone were supplied by the engine builders in the earliest days, the engine structure being built from local materials.

This policy of developing special skills persisted as long as engines were built, so that every shop had its particular fitters for guides, valve gear, connecting-rod bearings, or crossheads, and it was these men's pride in the finish which gave us so much lovely work. A case in point was Pollitt & Wigzells, where the top crosshead slide was held by large countersunk screws, the heads of which were often individually bedded in the holes to make the screw slots in the heads follow a straight line, and it was the expertise of such men that gave rapid production of sound engines.

Such work did not as a rule develop special physical characteristics in the men, but some machining processes did, so that Archie the planer, or Sam the shaper developed a crab-like gait from bending over to watch the cutter at work, while Bill the borer, too, could no doubt be identified after watching the ceaseless cutting of glass-hard cylinders. Knouty (cross grained) though they often were, they were craftsmen by nature as well as need, and they passed the special skills to the apprentices, who early learned that the right way was the best way. The sky was long clouded for the unfortunate who broke a tap in a nearly finished job; it could happen to anyone, but the need for peace and well being necessitated that it should not be you.

Two plates will serve to illustrate shops which each built engines and boilers and how, in 50 years, constructional facilities changed.

73 (a) **Fairbairn's Manchester** works of the 1840s shows how some of the processes of making boilers, land and marine engines, were carried out in the same workshop, although no doubt erecting was in a separate part. The business closed in the 1870s, but the conditions shown were typical of the early works.

(b) **Daniel Adamson's** engine shops in the 1890s. Showing the interesting feature of the steam engine driving the shafting of the shop (which did not build marine engines), this illustrates how boilermaking and plate work are now completely separated into their separate departments, where boilerinaking continued for 50 years after engine making ceased.

73a

73b

ENGINE TYPES

Horizontal Engines

Cross Compound

Inverted Vertical Engines

Triple Expansion

Compound

Uniflow

Horizontal Tandem

Single Crank

Twin Tandem

Other Types

Willans

Langworthy Bros, Salford (Willans & Robinson, 1904)　　　39

Manhattan

Hall Lane Mill, Leigh (Geo Saxon, 1914)　　　65

Turbine

Elk Mill, Royton (C. Parsons, 1926)　　　66

MAKERS

(numbers relate to plates)

Adamson, Daniel & Co, 21, 40, 59, 60	Marsdens Engines, 16
Ashton, Frost & Co, 13	Marsland, 57
Browett & Lindley, 35	McNaught, J. & W., 14, 29
Buckley & Taylor, 3, 15, 28	Musgrave, 24, 46, 48
Burnley Ironworks, 20, 41	Newton, Bean & Mitchell, 18
Carels, 26	Parsons, 66
Carmichael, James, 62	Petrie, J., 30
Clayton, J 4	Pollitt & Wigzell, 1, 17, 43, 49, 54, 55, 56
Clayton & Goodfellows, 7, 57	Roberts, Wm & Co, 2, 6
Coates, Victor, 36	Robey, 51
Cole, Booth & Porter, 64	Saxon, Geo, 10, 32, 52, 53, 65
Cole, Marchent & Morley, 37, 55	Scott & Hodgson, 22, 31
Douglas & Grant, 50, 61	Stott, S. S. & Co, 9
Foster, J., 8	Willans, 39
Fairbaim, Lawson, 44	Wood, J. & E., 19, 33
Fullerton, Hodgart & Barclay, 63	Wood Bros, 38, 42
Galloways, 27	Woodhouse & Mitchell, 54
Goodfellows & Matthews, 58	Yates, W. & J., 5
Hargreaves, Hick, 12, 23, 45	Yates & Thom, 11, 34, 47
Jessop, 25	